Right-Brained Fractions

a Forget Memorization book

Effortless learning through images, stories, hands-on activities, and patterns

by Sarah K Major

www.child1st.com

Right-Brained Fractions

© 2014 Sarah K Major

ISBN: 978-1-936981-97-7

Printed in the United States of America

To request more information regarding the copyright policy, contact:
Child1st Publications
800-881-0912
info@child1st.com

For other teaching and learning resources designed for visual, tactile, kinesthetic and other right-brained learners, visit www.child1st.com.

Other books and materials by this author:

Right-Brained Multiplication & Division
Right-Brained Addition & Subtraction
Right-Brained Place Value, Adding and Subtracting Multi-Digit Numbers
Alphabet Tales
The Illustrated Book of Sounds & Their Spelling Patterns
The Easy-for-Me™ Readers, sets A, B, and C
The Easy-for-Me™ Reading Program *Writing the Visual, Kinesthetic and Auditory Alphabet*
SnapWords® sight word cards and SnapLetters™ stylized alphabet
I Can Sing from 1 to 10
SnapWords® Spelling Dictionary

ABOUT THIS BOOK

This book is for children who are strongly visual, who learn all at once through pictures, are drawn to patterns, rely on body motions, and who need to understand the process behind each math problem they solve. Child1st teaching and learning resources all follow the principle of conveying teaching using a variety of right-brain-friendly elements. We take learning concepts that utilize symbols (numbers and letters) and abstractions, which are left-brained, and embed them in right-brained elements to beautifully integrate the left and right hemispheres in the brain.

Right-brained Elements:

1 - We embed symbols in **VISUALS** so that the child can take a quick look, absorb the learning piece, and store it as an image to be retrieved intact later.

2 - We use **PERSONIFICATION** which is a powerful element in teaching and learning. The use of personification makes for rapid learning because the very look and personality of the character conveys the substance of the learning. For example, in this book, Numerator, Denominator, Mixed Number and Improper Fraction are all characters.

3 - We rely on **PATTERN DISCOVERY** as a way of making numbers come alive and as a means of conveying the amazing relationships between numbers. What results is number sense. Because the brain is a pattern seeking organ, it is drawn to material that follows patterns. It is my desire that through this teaching resource, many children who are overwhelmed or daunted by math might come to truly be fascinated by it instead.

4 - We use **STORY** to contain and convey the meaning of what we are teaching. Stories, like visuals, make learning unforgettable. They explain the "why" behind math concepts and tie everything together, creating a vehicle for meaning and for recall.

5 - We use **BODY MOTION**—both gesture and whole body movement that mirrors the symbol shape or the action in the math story (such as addition or subtraction). Again, body movement is a powerful agent for learning and remembering. For many people, body motion makes recall effortless if the idea in the lesson is directly tied to a unique motion.

6 - We employ **VISUALIZATION**—a powerful tool for right-brain-dominant learners. If these learners are given time to transfer the image on the paper in front of them to their brains (prompt them to close their eyes and SEE it in their mind's eye), they will be able to retrieve that image later. If the image contains learning concepts, this is how they will remember what you want them to learn. So in this book, each time a visual is introduced, prompt the student(s) to "see" the image in their mind, eyes closed.

Some key practices to follow include:

- allowing plenty of time for **practice**
- focusing on **developing understanding** of what is going on in the process of computing with fractions
- encouraging the children to focus on understanding the **process** rather than just solving problems correctly
- avoiding the introduction of **rules** to memorize; rather, giving the children practice and then working with them to distill from their work a rule that might apply to what they did.
- if students need to **sharpen skills and gain fluency** with addition, subtraction, multiplication & division before diving into fractions, please go to our other Right-Brained math books. www.child1st.com/math.

Timeline for learning:

Traditionally the timeline for learning fractions is as follows:
- Kindergarten to grade 4 - introduce the concept of fractions minimally
- Grade 4 - include simple adding and subtracting of fractions
- Grade 5 - teach all operations of fractions
- Grades 6-8 - review and reteach all operations of fractions

It is possible, however, that using right-brained elements, your children will understand the process of working with fractions earlier than traditionally expected. While there is no enormous value in getting younger and younger children to learn fractions, it is amazing to see just how much children can learn when we use images, body motion, hands-on activities, and when we allow them to take their time to understand what is really going on. So, dig in, and be prepared to be surprised at what your students can do!

TABLE OF CONTENTS

Goals for This Chapter:

1. To learn the meaning of a whole upon which to base fractional parts.
2. To learn the terms "area," "set," and "length" as types of wholes.
3. To learn the meaning of the term "fraction."
4. To learn that fractional parts must be both fair and equal.

© 2000 Sarah Major

See Resource 1-0 for larger copy.

Introduce concepts in this book using stories. The storyline is always going to appear with a yellow background so you can find it easily! If you prefer, you can tell it in your own words.

Angela and Ben planted a pumpkin seed one spring. The rains fell, the sun shone, a beautiful vine sprouted and grew, spreading generously across the garden. When the kids saw the pumpkin vine bloom, they picked off all the blossoms except for one. They wanted to grow just one huge pumpkin to share with their six cousins!

The day finally came when they were ready to pick their pumpkin. Angela and Ben had a perfect plan! They would cut their gorgeous pumpkin into pieces following the lines they could see on the sides of their pumpkin. That way they and each of their cousins could have one section.

In just one day the cousins would come to visit and Angela and Ben were so excited! Dad had promised the kids that they could have a painting party and paint the backyard fence with their cousins. Each one of them would take a section of the fence to paint. Dad had already bought eight brushes so each child could have their own brush to use.

Mom and Dad were going to cook up a big pot of spaghetti for dinner when the fence was all painted. Spaghetti was their absolute favorite meal!

Finally the cousins arrived! Angela and Ben wanted to share their pumpkin pieces with their cousins right away, but their cousins couldn't wait to paint the fence! So Angela gave everyone a brush and a bucket of paint and told each one where to paint.

Here is a picture of the back yard and the section of fence that each child painted. (See Resource 1-0 for larger copy.)

Angela and Ben meant well! They loved to share, to do things together, and to include their cousins. But based on what is happening so far, do you think there will be a problem with anything? We'll see what happens in just a little bit!

I. What does "whole" mean?

When we say "whole" it means nothing is missing. If you eat the whole thing it means nothing is left over. Some "wholes" are big and some are tiny. We talk about "wholes" a lot! ***Here are some examples:***

1. I can't believe I ate the **whole** thing!
2. The **whole** family came together.
3. We get to paint the **whole** fence today!
4. We ate the **whole** bag of chips!
5. So much snow fell, it covered the **whole** car!
6. I am sick and my **whole** body aches.

Angela and Ben have a **whole** pumpkin to share. They live in a house with a fence running around the **whole** back yard. Their family has a **whole** set of 10 blue dishes in the kitchen. So Angela and Ben already know a lot about **wholes**. But now, let's go back to the story and see what happens.

By 4:00, five of the children had finished their section of the fence. The other three weren't finished yet. Mom called from the back door to say that dinner would be ready in 30 minutes, so the children who were finished decided to jump in and help those who were not finished painting yet.

At dinner, Dad served spaghetti. Because there were so many people, they used the whole set of 10 dishes! They ate the whole bowl of spaghetti, too! Dad started out really piling the plates, but the more plates he served, the less he served because the spaghetti was running out! Here is what their table looked like. Can you tell which plate Dad served first and which he served last?

Three kinds of wholes

Let's think back over what has happened so far. There were three wholes that Ben and Angela shared with their family: a whole pumpkin, the whole fence, and the pot of spaghetti which was served on the whole set of dishes. Those "wholes" don't look anything alike, but they show us the three different kinds of "wholes" there are.

The pumpkin kind of "whole" is called AREA.

Other examples of AREA are:
1. A pizza
2. A cake or pie
3. A football field
4. A sheet of paper

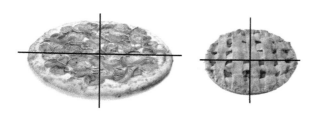

Hint: You can cut them two ways - sideways and up and down.

7

The snake kind of "whole" is called LENGTH.

Other examples of LENGTH are:

1. A peppermint stick
2. A licorice whip
3. A tape measure
4. Train tracks

 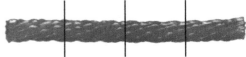

Hint: We usually cut them side by side. Chop, chop, chop.

The dishes kind of "whole" is called SET.

Other examples of SETS are:

1. A matchbox car collection
2. A lego set
3. Silverware
4. Crayons

Hint: They are loose items of the same kind that belong together.

Spend some time with the students, gathering examples of each kind of whole. Area could be things as simple as a sheet of paper, a paper plate, a fruit roll-up, or a desk top. Length could be a ruler, a hallway, a belt, a ribbon, or a bulletin board border. Sets could be a stack of books, pencils, crayons, or paperclips. If you treat this as a scavenger hunt, the students would enjoy the exercise very much. Make evenly matched teams and ask them to find examples of all three kinds of wholes. Set a time limit and then let each group share what they found.

Hands On:

Use Resource 1-1 to practice differentiating between different types of "wholes."

II. What does "fraction" mean?

When we say "fraction" it means a "whole" broken into pieces.

Other words that mean parts of a whole are:

1. parts

2. pieces

3. chunks

Look at the picture below. The word "fraction" fell and broke into pieces. Now instead of a whole word, we have pieces of the word.

See Resource 1-0 for larger image.

© 2014 Sarah Major

Fair and equal shares

Think back together over what has happened so far. Three times Ben and Angela meant to share things fairly but didn't manage to do so. The pumpkin sections were all different **sizes**, the sections of fence were not all the same **length**, and when the spaghetti was served, not everyone got the same **amount**.

Sometimes it doesn't matter if you share something with others and the parts you share are not all the same. But there will be times you will need to be sure **everyone gets the same amount** of something or you might hear people saying, "That's not fair! You got more than me!" In order to make **fair and equal shares**,

we study something called fractions. In the picture of the word "fraction" the pieces are not equally sized. The word got "fractured" or broken, but the pieces are not fair and equal shares.

III. What do fair and equal shares look like?

What would happen if you and your friends decided to order a pizza to eat and instead of cutting it in pieces that are the same size the pizza store cut some pieces really small and others really big? Would your friends like getting the small pieces? Having the pieces not be the same size might cause a bit of a problem.

Look at the pizzas below. Which pizza will be easier to share with your friends? The first one or the second one?

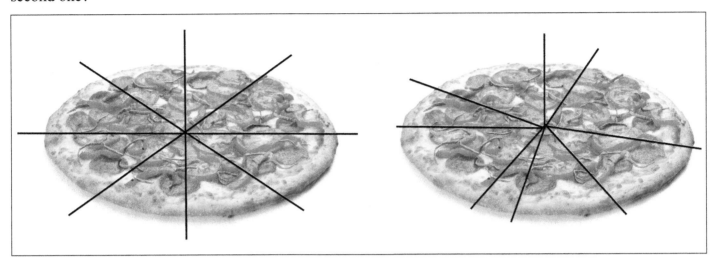

The first pizza has fair shares and would be really easy to share.

Critical thinking

When Ben and Angela wanted to share the pumpkin fairly with their cousins, why did the pieces come out unequal, and what could they have done to make sure everyone got a fair share?

What about painting the back yard fence? How could the children have divided up the work so everyone got the same length of fence to paint?

Finally, when Dad served up the spaghetti, what would you suggest he do to make sure each person had a fair share?

Hands On:

Use Resource 1-2 to have children identify which items are fair shares. For those that are not fair and equal shares, discuss with the child how they might divide the shape to make it fair.

Next use Resource 1-3 to have children think about how to divide items into fair shares. Discuss with them other ways to share each picture. For instance, how would they share the graham crackers with four kids? With 9 children? They would have to break each cracker into its three pieces and then split them up. Supply real graham crackers to use for tactile activities with area, gummy bears for set, and licorice whips for length. Finally, use Resource 1-4 to assess your students' knowledge.

© 2000 Sarah Major

© 2014 Sarah Major

1-1 What kind of whole is this?

Under each picture below, write whether the whole is AREA, LENGTH, or SET.

Name_____

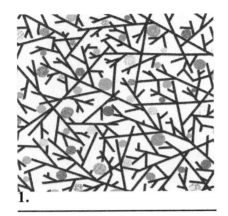

1. _____

2. _____

3. _____

4. _____

5. _____

6. _____

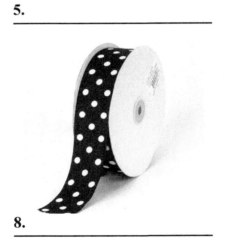

7. _____

8. _____

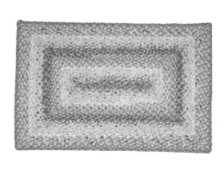

9. _____

10. _____

11. _____

12. _____

1-2 Recognizing fair & equal shares

Name_____

Look at each model. If a model does not show fair and equal shares, mark it with a big X.

1.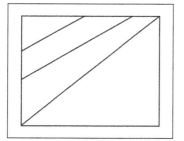

6.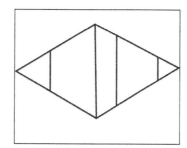

2.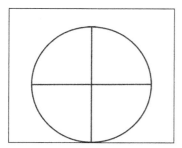

7.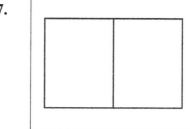

3.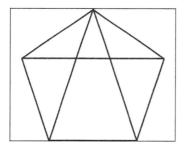

8.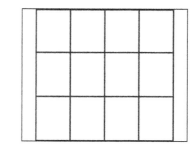

4.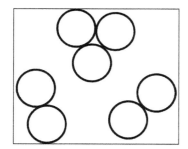

9.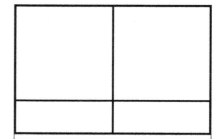

5.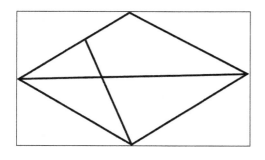

10.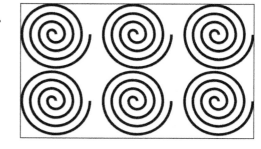

1-3 Practicing fair & equal shares

How could you share each of the "wholes" below so you have fair and equal shares. Use your pencil to circle fair shares.

1. Fair and equal shares for 3 kids.

2. Fair and equal shares for 3 kids.

3. Fair and equal shares for 4 kids.

4. Fair and equal shares for 2 kids.

5. Fair and equal shares for 10 kids.

6. Fair and equal shares for 4 kids.

1-4 What I have learned about wholes & fractional parts   Name_____

Label each picture with the kind of "whole" it is:

1. _____

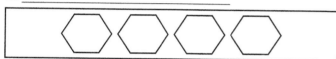

2. _____

3. _____

Circle the pictures that show fair and equal shares:

4.

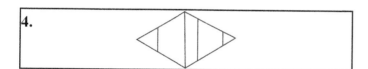

5.

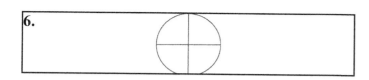

6.

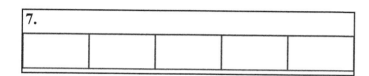

7.

8.

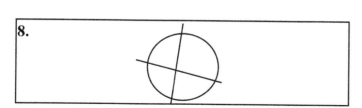

Divide the wholes to make fair and equal shares. Use a ruler if needed.

9. Fair and equal shares for 4 kids.

10. Fair and equal shares for 8 kids.

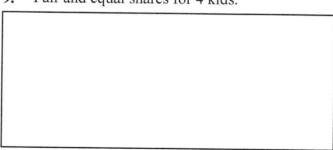

11. Circle fair and equal shares for 5 kids.

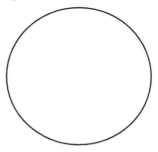

12. Circle fair and equal shares for 3 kids.

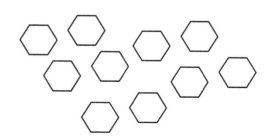

13. What does "fraction" mean?

17

FRACTIONAL PARTS

Goals for This Chapter:

1. To read and write names of fractional parts.
2. To identify fractional parts within a whole.
3. To divide a whole into fractional parts.
4. To make models of fractional parts.

I. Read and write fractional parts

Now that we've talked about wholes, fractions, and fair shares, we need to learn the names for fractional parts. Give the students Resource 2-1 which shows rows divided into fractional parts and labeled with their names. Explain that fractional parts are named according to how many parts there are in the whole.

For help with spelling the names of fractional parts, point out the relationship between the name of the **number** and the name of the corresponding **fractional part.** For example, FOURTHS, SIXTHS, SEVENTHS, EIGHTHS all have the whole number word inside of them with a few letters added at the end. THREE and THIRDS and FIVE and FIFTHS only have the first two letters in common. WHOLE and HALVES are totally different from their number words (ONE and TWO). Point out also that if we continue writing more fractional words, the pattern will continue: NINTHS, TENTHS, ELEVENTHS, TWELFTHS and so forth. Be sure to point out that NINE drops the E to become NINTHS.

See Resource 2-1 for a larger chart.

	Whole
	Halves
	Thirds
	Fourths
	Fifths
	Sixths
	Sevenths
	Eighths

II. Identify fractional parts

In this section, students will practice identifying fractional parts from within a whole. A basic ground rule to review is that for pieces of a whole to be fractional parts, they have to also be fair shares. Some parts cannot be large and some small. They all have to be the same size. Our goal in this section is for the students to learn to identify the fractional part by counting how many parts there are in all.

One of the difficulties students have with fractions is that they don't know to identify the fractional part before writing the fraction. Often they will put the number of parts selected in the numerator and the number of parts left over in the denominator. So it is critical at this point that they understand that the name of the fractional part is a reflection of how many parts there are in the whole.

For example, in this fraction model, a student might think the green space is the numerator while the white spaces left over are the denominator. So their fraction would be 1/3 instead of 1/4.

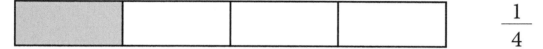

$$\frac{1}{4}$$

It is for this reason that we will have plenty of practice with just identifying fractional parts by name rather than rushing right into making fractions.

Hands On:
Use Resource 2-3 A - B to practice identifying and writing the names of fractional parts.

III. Making fractional parts

This section is very hands-on. The students will use models of wholes found in Resource 2-4 A - C. The point of this activity is for the students to learn to divide wholes into specific fractional parts.

It is also important to help students learn how to sketch their own models in case they are solving problems and don't have premade models. Show them how to make the fractional parts with their bodies, then have them practice drawing them in a clock face. Here are motions for thirds, fourths, fifths, and sixths.

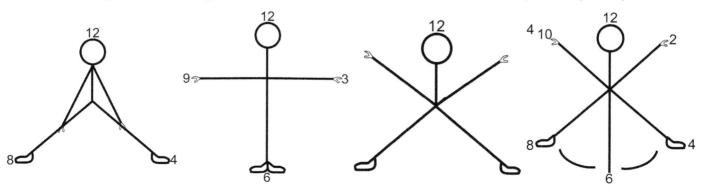

19

Give the students graph paper and this time, let them use colored markers to create wholes that are divided into fractional parts. For example, they will be asked to show a whole that is divided into sixths. So they will draw a line around six squares on the graph paper.

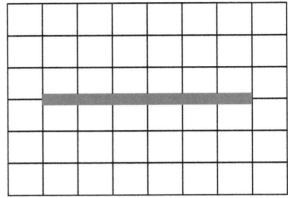

Their wholes don't have to be simple grids as long as the correct number of fractional parts are displayed. They will be instructed to show AREA, LENGTH, and SETS. Length is demonstrated in the example to the right.

See the examples of area and sets below.

The first shows area and is a whole divided into sixteenths, while the second is a set of sixths.

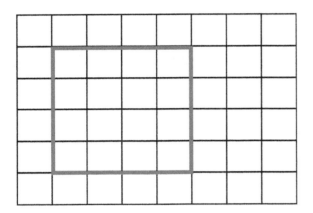
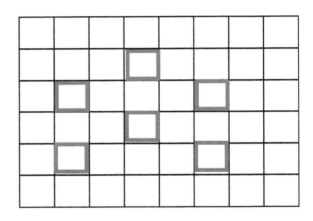

Hands On:

Use Resource 2-5 Wholes and fractional parts.

Hands On:

When you feel the students are ready, assess their knowledge using Resource 2-6 What I know about fractional parts.

2-1 Models and names of fractional parts

Name_____

Color-coding highlights relationship of number names to names of fractional parts. ONE relates to WHOLE, TWO relates to HALVES, THREE relates to THIRDS, FOUR to FOURTHS, FIVE to FIFTHS, SIX to SIXTHS, SEVEN to SEVENTHS, EIGHT to EIGHTHS, NINE to NINTHS, etc. Color-coding is helpful to many students. Blue letters show the relationship of the names of the numbers to their related fractional part. Green letters show the pattern of endings on many of the fractional parts.

Whole

Halves

Thirds

Fourths

Fifths

Sixths

Sevenths

Eighths

2-2 Writing the names of fractional parts

Beside each number name, write the name of the fractional part that goes with it.

One _____   Six _____

Two _____   Seven _____

Three _____   Eight _____

Four _____   Nine _____

Five _____   Ten _____

....

Next, count the fractional parts for each problem, and write the name of the fractional part below each model.

1. _____   5. _____

2. _____   6. _____

3. _____   7. _____

4. _____

2-3 A Models and names of fractional parts

Name_____

For each of the models below, find the fractional part and write its name on the line.

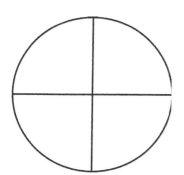

1. _____

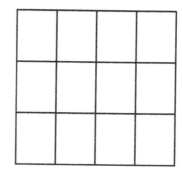

5. _____

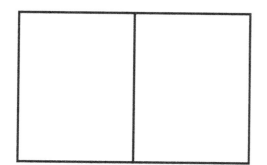

2. _____

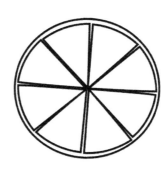

6. _____

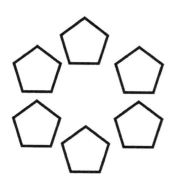

3. _____

7. _____

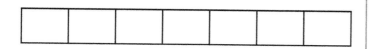

4. _____

8. _____

2-3 B Models and names of fractional parts

Name_____

For each of the models below, find the fractional part and write its name on the line

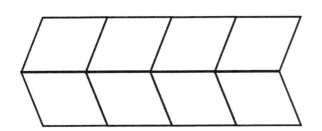

1. _____

5. _____

2. _____

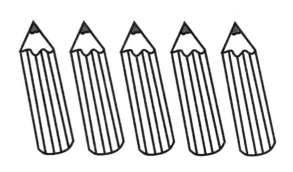

6. _____

3. _____

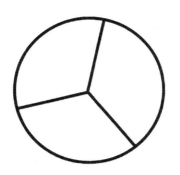

7. _____

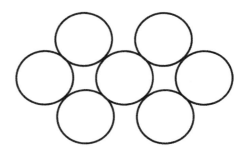

4. _____

8. _____

2-4 A making fractional parts

Name_____

Cut out the circle and fold it to make the fractional parts listed below. Each number marks 5 sections just like minutes on a clock face.

1. Fold the clockface to show halves. Use a colored marker and ruler to mark the fold line.

2. Fold the clockface to show fourths. Use a different color of marker to mark the new fold line.

3. Fold the clockface to show eighths. Use a different color of marker to mark the new fold lines.

4. Fold the clockface to show sixteenths. Use a different color of marker to mark the new fold lines.

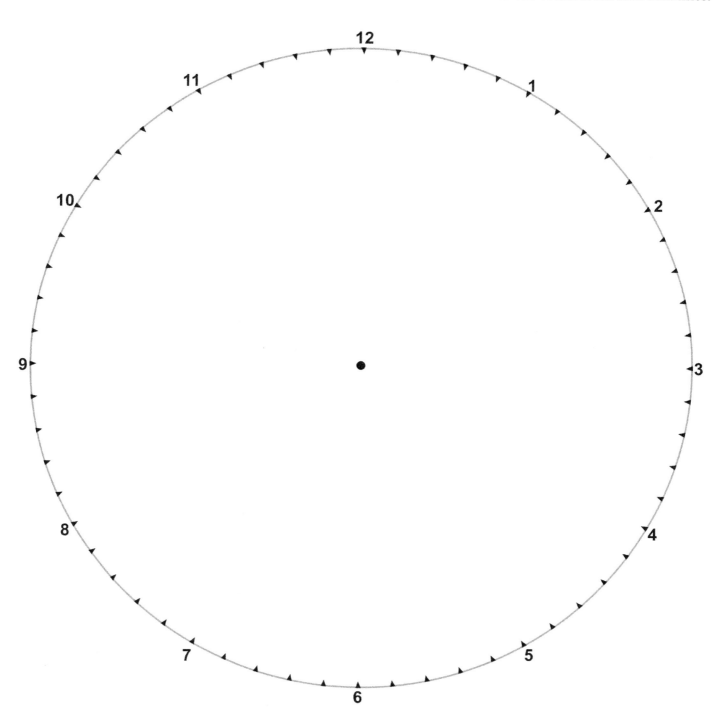

2-4 B Making fractional parts

Name_____

Cut out the circle and fold it to make the fractional parts listed below.

1. Show thirds. Use a colored marker and ruler to mark the lines.

2. Show sixths with a different colored marker.

3. Show twelfths using a third color.

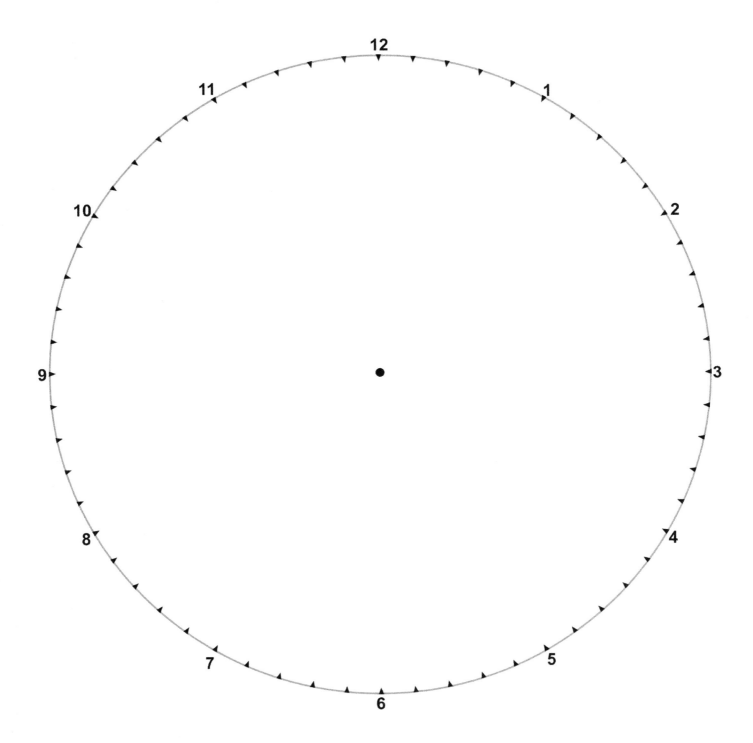

2-4 C Making fractional parts

Cut out the strips and fold them to make the fractional parts listed below.

1a. Fold the strip to show halves. Use a colored marker and ruler to mark the fold line.

b. Fold the strip to show fourths. Use a colored marker and ruler to mark the new fold lines.

c. Fold the strip to show eighths. Use a colored marker and ruler to mark the new fold lines.

d. Fold the strip to show sixteenths. Use a colored marker and ruler to mark the new fold lines.

2a. Fold the strip to show thirds. Use a colored marker and ruler to mark the fold line.

b. Fold the strip to show sixths. Use a colored marker and ruler to mark the new fold lines.

c. Fold the strip to show ninths. Use a colored marker and ruler to mark the new fold lines.

d. Fold the strip to show twelfths. Use a colored marker and ruler to mark the new fold lines.

2-5 Wholes and fractional parts

In each problem below, draw a line on or around squares on the graph to show the whole. The whole might show area, length, or set.

1. Draw an "area whole" for sixths.

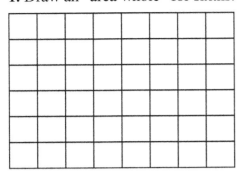

2. Draw a "length whole" for fourths.

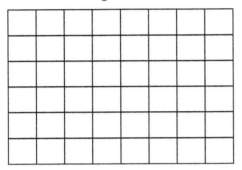

3. Draw a "set whole" for eighths.

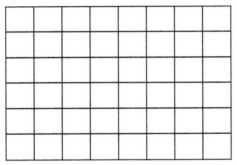

4. Draw a "length whole" for fifths.

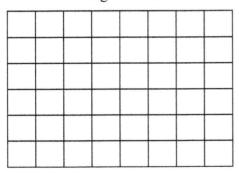

5. Draw a "set whole" for sevenths.

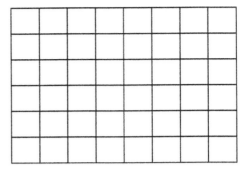

6. Draw an "area whole" for tenths.

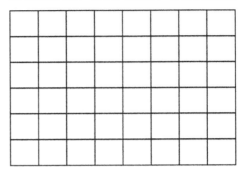

7. Draw a "length whole" for thirds.

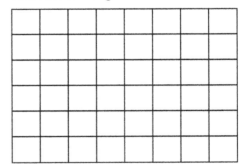

8. Draw an "area whole" for ninths.

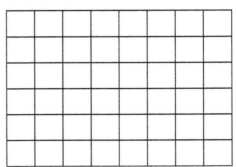

2-6 What I have learned about fractional parts.

Name_____

1. Label each row with the name of that fractional part:

Identify and then write the fractional parts:

2. _____

6. _____

3. _____

7. _____

4. _____

8. _____

5. _____

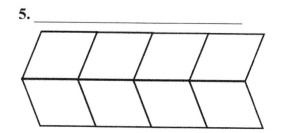

9. _____

10. _____

NUMERATOR & DENOMINATOR

Goals for This Chapter:

1. To read and write "numerator" and "denominator."
2. To understand the meaning and function of each.
3. To create a fraction with numerator and denominator from a model.
4. To turn a word problem into a fraction with numerator and denominator.

I. Meet Brothers Num & Nom Ators

Show the students the Ator Brothers on the next page. Num Ator is all about numbers and counting. He loves to count. Point out that the word "number" is almost all there inside "numerator." All that is lacking is the letter B. Num Ator counts, thinks about counting, and dreams about counting.

Next, introduce Nom Ator. Nom is all about names and naming things. "Nom" sounds a tiny bit like "name." Beyond that, the word NOMBRE means NAME in Spanish. NOME is NAME in Italian and in Portuguese. So Nom, with his wide open mouth, is all about naming things.

Believe me when I say that this is not just a silly story with sillier pictures. The Ator Brothers bring great significance to the study of fractions. This duo might even be the missing link for students who struggle with fractions.

The Ator Brothers' last name has a special meaning also. ATOR means "one who." So Num Ator is "the one who counts," while Nom Ator means "the one who names."

Share with your students other ATOR family members:

Activator	One who activates
Agitator	One who agitates
Allocator	One who allocates
Aviator	One who flies
Calculator	One who calculates
Creator	One who creates
Decorator	One who decorates
Cultivator	One who cultivates

Challenge your students to get online and do a search for "words ending in ator" and then have them look up the meaning of words they find. There is a pattern there!

Remind them these characters they find are all relatives of the Ator Brothers, Nom and Num.

Find photos of Num and Nom on the next page.

The Ator Brothers:

numerator

De' counter

denominator

De' Namer

alicia kevin darren sue rachel oliver jaxson cookie angela kara ben fred jacob henry deshawn samantha abbie evelyn luke justin keysha

© 2000 Sarah Major

II. Let's put Num & Nom in their places

The Ator Brothers share a house. Num lives upstairs while Nom lives downstairs. Nom is the one who NAMES the fractional part we are using (how many parts the whole was cut into), while Num is the one who COUNTS how many fractional parts we are going to use. First we enter the house downstairs where we name the fractional part, then we climb the stairs where we count how many parts we will use. (*See a photo of the Ator Brothers at home on the next page*).

Characters:

I COUNT the fractional parts we will use.

I NAME the fractional parts in the whole.

*For a reminder, explain to students that a very young child first learns to **name** things before he learns to **count** things.*

Now look at the model below. Models of Fractions show how many parts the whole was cut into, and the orange dots tell us how many of the parts we are actually going to use. There is only one orange dot on each model, so the **numerator** will be 1 in each fraction. The Symbols show "how many" on top and "of what" on the bottom. Point out that the more pieces the whole is cut into, the bigger the **denominator** becomes!

Models of Fractions:	Words:	Symbols:
	One Half	$\dfrac{1}{2}$
	One Third	$\dfrac{1}{3}$
	One Fourth	$\dfrac{1}{4}$
	One Fifth	$\dfrac{1}{5}$

Hands On:

Use Resource 3-1 to practice the names and roles of the Ator Brothers.

The Ator Brothers at home:

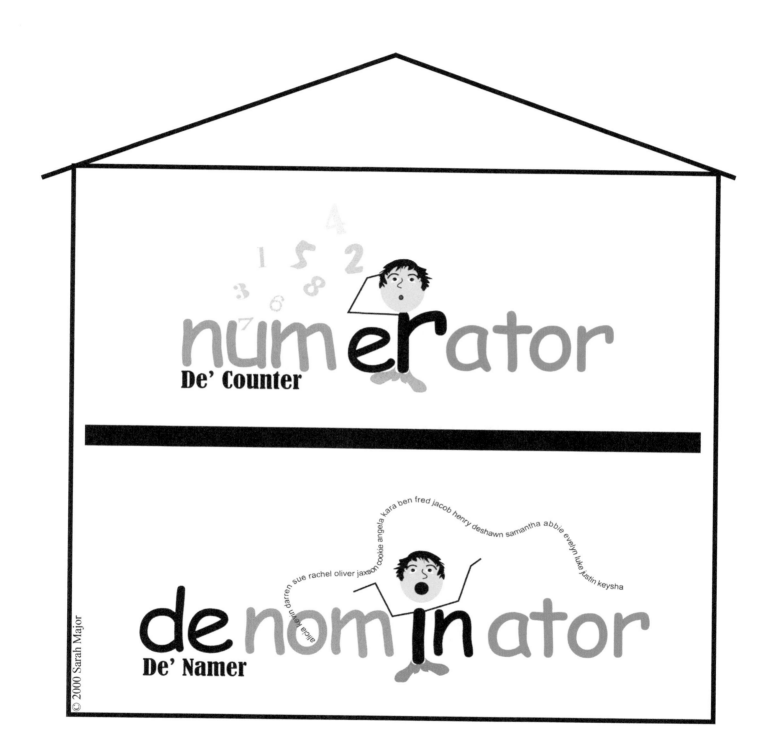

Hands On:

Give students Resource 3-2 to use for Section III.

III. Let's put Num & Nom to work

After you have had time to thoroughly become acquainted with Num and Nom, let's get to the fun part of fractions! We are going to make models of fractions first and then will put that information into fractions using symbols. Before we do that, be sure each child can write the terms correctly, and make sure they know that ATOR means "one who...", that NUM deals with counting, while NOM names the fractional parts. Use Resource 3-1 again if needed.

Example from real life: You have 12 tools in your toolbox, but for this job you will only use 3. So you will use 3/12 of your tools.

Working orally, go through the following models. **First** ask for the word that names the fractional part. Write that word under the line. **Next**, count the number of fractional parts that are orange. Write that number above the line. Finally, change the words to symbols as shown below.

The students' copy has an additional problem not shown here.

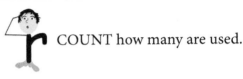

COUNT how many are used.

_____

NAME the fractional part (or how many parts in all).

1	1
Half	2
2	2
Thirds	3
1	1
Fourth	4
4	4
Fifths	5
2	2
Sixths	6
3	3
Sevenths	7

34

Hands On:

Use Resource 3-3 From models to fractions. Next, using real materials, pair the students up. They will take turns making a fraction model for their partner to represent using numbers.

IV. From word problems to fractions

In order for children to really understand fractions, they will have to be able to use them in real life situations. In this section, we are going to create word problems, use real materials, and we are going to work through turning each mini-story into a fraction that just uses symbols.

To begin with, copy Resource 3-4 so that each student has a copy. Share that in a word problem, there are usually three parts: the story, the question, and the answer.

Here are word problems:

1. Our dog had a litter of 8 puppies.
All the puppies were black except for three who have white feet.
How would you write a fraction that shows how many puppies have white feet?

$$\frac{3}{8}$$

      Ask: "What kind of "whole" is this?" [Set - a set of puppies]

      Ask: "What is the fractional part?" [Eighths - 8 pups in all]

      Ask: "Where does this number go? Above or below the line?" [Eighths is the name of the fractional part, the denominator, so it goes below the line. Remember we name first.]

      Ask: "How many puppies have white feet?" [3. We have gone upstairs to count.]

      Ask: "Where do we write this number?" [This answers the question "how many are we talking about, so it is the numerator and goes upstairs or above the line.]

We want the students to picture what is happening in each story. They will be looking for three things: two numbers and a question. In the puppy story, the first number is 8 puppies in all, the second number is 3 have white feet, and the question is going to direct your attention to what we are talking about.

2. I have a huge chocolate chip cookie that I cut into six pieces.
Two of my friends came over and all 3 of us want to eat a piece of cookie.
How would you write a fraction to show how many pieces of cookie will be eaten?

$$\frac{3}{6}$$

      Ask: "What kind of "whole" is this?" [Area - one cookie]

      Ask: "What is the fractional part?" [Sixths - cookie was cut into 6 pieces]

      Ask: "Where does this number go? Above or below the line?" [Sixths is the name of the fractional part, the denominator, so it goes downstairs, or below the line.]

      Ask: "How many pieces of cookie will get eaten?" [3 - one for me and 2 for my friends]

      Ask: "Where do we write this number?" [This answers the question "how many are we talking about, so it is the numerator and goes upstairs, or above the line.]

Hands On:
Use Resource 3-5 From stories to fractions. Take it further by asking kids to make up word problems for a partner to write in fraction form.

Here are more word problems:

Use these word problems to cement the meaning of fractions in your students' heads. Enlist students to make up word problems to pose to the others. Encourage the students to use real materials or to draw little pictures if this will help them work out what is happening in each story. For each story, ask what kind of whole we are dealing with and how to write the fraction.

1. Main Street is 12 blocks long. Both my friend and I live on that street. When I go to his house, I have to walk 5 blocks. How would you write a fraction that shows how many blocks I have to walk?
[Whole is LENGTH. Fraction is 5/12]

2. We ordered a pizza cut into 8 pieces. Three of us ate one piece each. How would you write a fraction that shows how many pieces of pizza were eaten?
[Whole is AREA. Fraction is 3/8]

3. I have 15 cousins. 7 of them live in my town and are coming over for the 4th of July. Write a fraction that shows how many of my cousins are coming over on the 4th of July.
[Whole is SET. Fraction is 7/15]

4. My brother has 10 baseball caps. Mom said he has to get rid of 4 of them, which he is not happy about. How would you write a fraction that shows the hats my brother has to get rid of?
[Whole is SET. Fraction is 4/10]

5. Mom cut the lasagne into 15 pieces. We ate 7 of the pieces. How would you show the number of pieces we ate in a fraction?
[Whole is AREA. Fraction is 7/15]

6. The track at school is 4 miles long. I ran 1 mile and walked the rest of the way. How would you write a fraction that shows how many miles I ran?
[Whole is LENGTH. Fraction is 1/4.]

Hands On:
Use Resource 3-6 Assessment

Name_____

1. Write Nom's full name _____.

2. What is Nom's job? _____.

3. Write Num's full name _____.

4. What is Num's job? _____,

5. Who lives upstairs in the house the brothers share? _____.

6. Who lives downstairs in the house the brothers share? _____.

7. What does "ator" mean? _____.

8. First figure out the fractional part, and then write a fraction for each model. The dot shows how many we are going to use.

Models of Fractional Parts: ## Fractions:

   ____

   ____

   ____

   ____

3-2 Models of fractional parts

First, write the word that names the fractional part under the line by each model. Next, count the number of fractional parts that are orange. Write that number above the line. Finally, change the words to symbols.

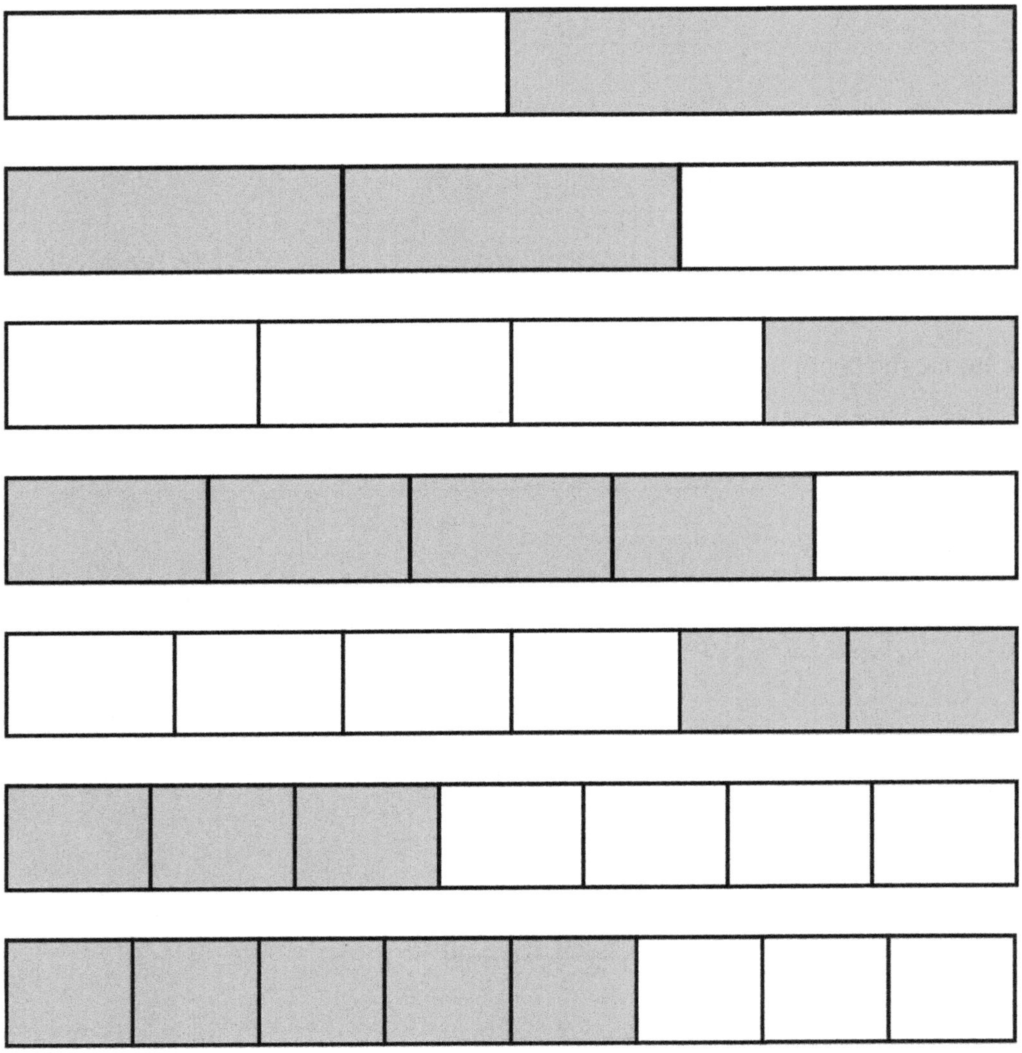

_____ ___

_____ ___

_____ ___

_____ ___

_____ ___

_____ ___

_____ ___

1. Write a fraction showing the number of fractional parts that are shaded.

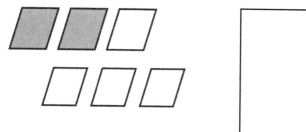

2. Write a fraction showing the number of fractional parts that are white.

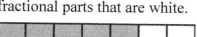

3. Write a fraction showing the number of fractional parts that are circled.

4. Write a fraction showing the number of fractional parts that are shaded.

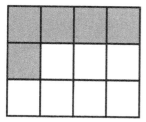 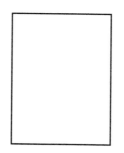

5. Write a fraction showing the number of fractional parts that are shaded.

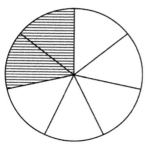 

6. Write a fraction showing the number of fractional parts that were eaten.

7. Write a fraction showing the number of fractional parts that are white.

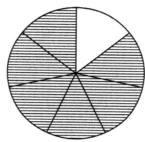 

8. Write a fraction showing the number of fractional parts that are white.

9. Write a fraction showing the number of fractional parts that are circled.

10. Write a fraction showing the number of fractional parts that are white.

3-4 Story problems 1

Name_____

Color the puppies to match the story. Now, write a fraction to show how many have white feet.

Cut the cookie into six pieces or draw lines to show 6 pieces. Next cross out the ones you and your friends ate. Write a fraction that shows the pieces that were eaten.

3-5 From stories to fractions

Name_____

Read each story below. Draw a picture of what is happening. Next, write a fraction that answers the question in the story.

1. My family has five bikes. Two are red and three are blue. Write a fraction that shows how many bikes are blue.

2. The park is an 8 acre rectangle. 3 of the acres are covered by a pond, while 5 acres are grassy. Write a fraction that shows how many of the acres are grassy.

3. The relay team has five runners. Three of the runners are boys and two are girls. Write a fraction that shows how many of the runners are girls.

4. Mom cut a pan of brownies into 12 pieces. We ate 7 of them for dinner. Write a fraction to show how many pieces we ate.

5. My class went on a field trip. There were 10 of us; six boys and four girls. Write a fraction to show how many of us are girls.

6. We have a roll of wrapping paper that is 100 feet long. We wrapped a lot of presents and used up 25 feet of paper. Write a fraction that shows how many feet of paper we used.

7. Darrah has bubble gum to share with her friends. She has 13 pieces to begin with. She gave away 3 pieces. Write a fraction to show how many pieces she gave away.

8. Melissa cut her apple into four pieces. She gave her friends three of them. Write a fraction to show how many pieces she kept.

9. We ordered a pizza which was cut into 8 pieces. We ate five pieces. Write a fraction to show how many pieces were left.

10. It is 12 blocks to Jaylen's house. I had walked five blocks when it started to rain. White a fraction that shows how many blocks I walked before I got wet!

Name_____

1. Write the real names of the Ator Brothers under each picture.

_____   _____

_____   _____

2. Under each name, write what that brother does.

3. Write a fraction for this model in the box:

4. Write a fraction for this model in the box:

5. Write a fraction for this model in the box:

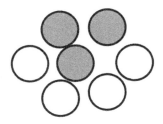

6. Color the model to show this fraction: $\frac{6}{8}$

7. Color the model to show this fraction: $\frac{2}{5}$

8. Color the model to show this fraction: $\frac{4}{7}$

9. I blew 9 bubbles and all of them popped except for 3. Write a fraction that shows how many bubbles did not pop.

10. I cut a long piece of string into 10 pieces. I used 7 of them to tie leaf bags shut. Write a fraction that shows how many pieces of string I used.

11. Draw a picture of a set of cookies and decide how many you will eat. Mark these with an X. Now write a fraction showing how many cookies you ate.

COUNTING & COMPARING FRACTIONS

Goals for This Chapter:

1. To learn that denominators must be the same when counting fractions
2. To understand how numerators change while counting.
3. To understand when and why denominators double
4. To learn that the bigger the denominator, the smaller the fractional part

I. Counting fractional parts:

What does it mean and what does it look like?

Num Ator went for a walk with his brother Nom. As they walked along Num started counting. He just couldn't help it!

He pointed to a tree and said, "One,"

to a rock and said, "Two,"

to a house and said, "Three,"

to a cloud and said, "Four."

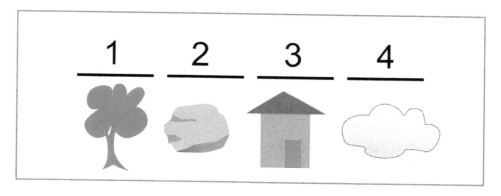

"STOP!" yelled Nom. "This isn't working! You can't count if you're switching what you're counting all the time! You can only count if you count the same kind of thing!"

"What?" asked Num.

"Never mind. I'll tell you what to count," said Nom, "and then you can only count that one thing until I name something else."

"OK. I can do that," said Num.

Nom said, "Trees. Count trees."

So Num started counting, "One tree, two trees, three trees," and so forth.

What he counted looked like this:

"Good!" said Nom, "Now count houses." So Num counted houses, "One house, two houses, three houses," and what he counted looked like this:

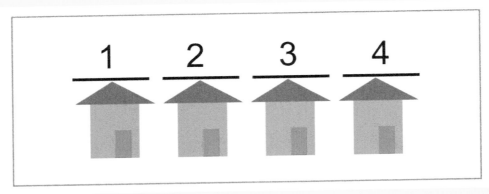

From that day on, when Num and Nom went walking they had a good time because each of them got to do their favorite thing! Numerator got to count and Denominator got to name! Num learned that when you count things, you have to count things that are alike.

II. Practice counting fractional parts:

Back at home, the Ator brothers were making dinner. They decided to make pizza from scratch. Nom's job was to mix the dough. Then Num would cut the dough into pieces and press each piece into a pizza pan. Nom came behind him adding pizza sauce and toppings, then Num slid the pizzas into the oven to bake. When the pizzas were done, Nom took a pizza cutter and cut each one into pieces. First Nom cut each pizza in half. As soon as Num saw the pieces, he excitedly began to count them. "One half, two halves, three halves," and so forth until he got to ten halves. Refer to Resource 4-1 for larger illustrations to share.

This is what the pizzas looked like:

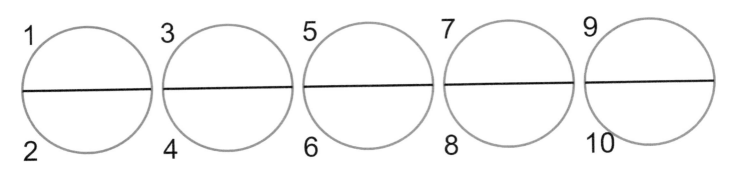

This is what it looked like when Num counted pizza halves:

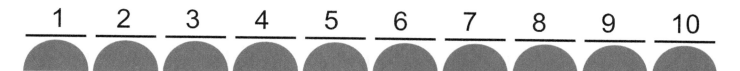

By the time Num finished counting, he saw that Nom had been busily cutting the pizzas again! "Now we have FOURTHS." said Nom.

Num was very excited that he could begin counting all over again. He said, "One fourth, two fourths, three fourths, four fourths, five fourths," and so on, until he got clear to "20 fourths."

This is what the pizzas looked like:

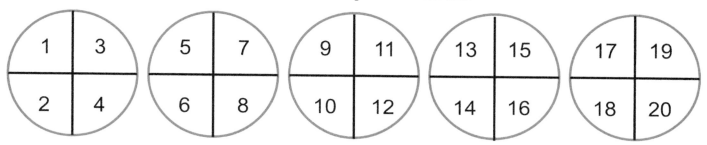

This is what it looked like when Num counted pizza fourths:

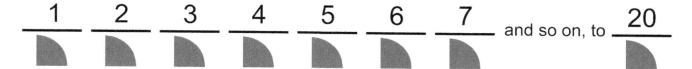

But just as soon as Num finished counting fourths, Nom cut the pizzas again and announced, "Now we have eighths!"

Num started in right away counting, "One eighth, two eighths, three eighths," all the way up to 40 eighths.

This is what the pizzas looked like:

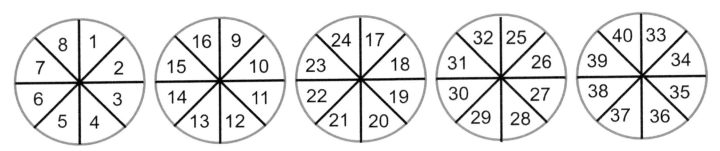

This is what it looked like when Num counted pizza eighths.

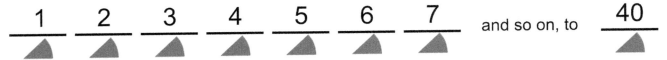

$\dfrac{1}{\blacktriangle}$ $\dfrac{2}{\blacktriangle}$ $\dfrac{3}{\blacktriangle}$ $\dfrac{4}{\blacktriangle}$ $\dfrac{5}{\blacktriangle}$ $\dfrac{6}{\blacktriangle}$ $\dfrac{7}{\blacktriangle}$ and so on, to $\dfrac{40}{\blacktriangle}$

Pause to reflect & discuss

What patterns can we find in the images in this story? Refer to Resource 4-1 for images.

1. What happens to the total number of pieces each time Nom cuts the pizzas?:

[They double. They go from 5 to 10 to 20 to 40 because each single piece is cut into 2 pieces.]

2. What is happening to the sizes of the pizza slices as the total number of slices gets bigger?

[You have 5 wholes, 10 halves, 20 fourths, 40 eighths. The total number is higher with each cut but the pieces get smaller and smaller. Half as small each time, in fact! So numerators double while denominators halve.]

3. If you wrote out what Num counted as a series of fractions, what would you see happening to the numerator?

[The numerator would start with 1 and increase one number at a time just like it does when he is counting.]

Hands On:
Use Resource 4-2 Counting fractional parts.

III. Comparing fractional parts:

Num and Nom were making pizza again, they had just taken one huge pizza out of the oven. Nom had just cut it in half when the doorbell rang.

It was Joe. Num and Nom decided to share their pizza with Joe.

Here's the pizza:

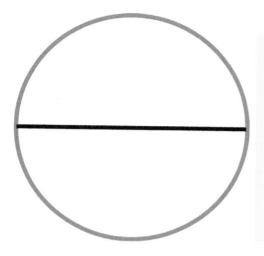
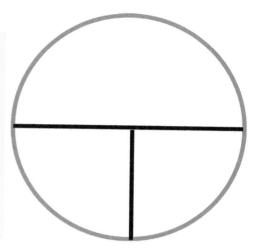

What should they do?
Num said, "Nom, cut
your half in half so Joe
can have a piece."
Was this fair and
equal shares?
No! Not a good idea.

Ask the kids what they would suggest: invite another person over? put a fourth of the pizza in the fridge? cut the extra fourth into 3 pieces?

Before the three guys could decide what to do, the doorbell rang and 5 more kids were at the door. How should Nom cut the pizza in order to feed 8 people? Give the children Resource 4-3 and have them make fair and equal shares for various scenarios as specified in the directions. When sharing with 8 or 4 people, they may simply fold the paper circles. But for 6 and 12, they will need to think about what to do.

Comparing fractional parts hands-on:

Hands On:
Use Resource 4-4 Comparing fractional parts. The questions to ask are just below.

1. Which is bigger? 1/4 or 1/6?   [1/4 is bigger].
2. Which is bigger? 1/5 or 1/8?   [1/5 is bigger].
3. Which is more? 2/5 or 2/7?   [2/5 is more].
4. Which is smaller? 1/3 or 1/4?   [1/4 is smaller].
5. Which is smaller? 2/9 or 1/3?   [2/9 is smaller].
6. Which is more? 3/4 or 5/8?   [3/4 is more].
7. Which is bigger? 3/11 or 4/12?   [4/12 is bigger].

Hands On:
Use Resource 4-5 What I know about comparing fractional parts.

4-1 Images for Chapter 4 story

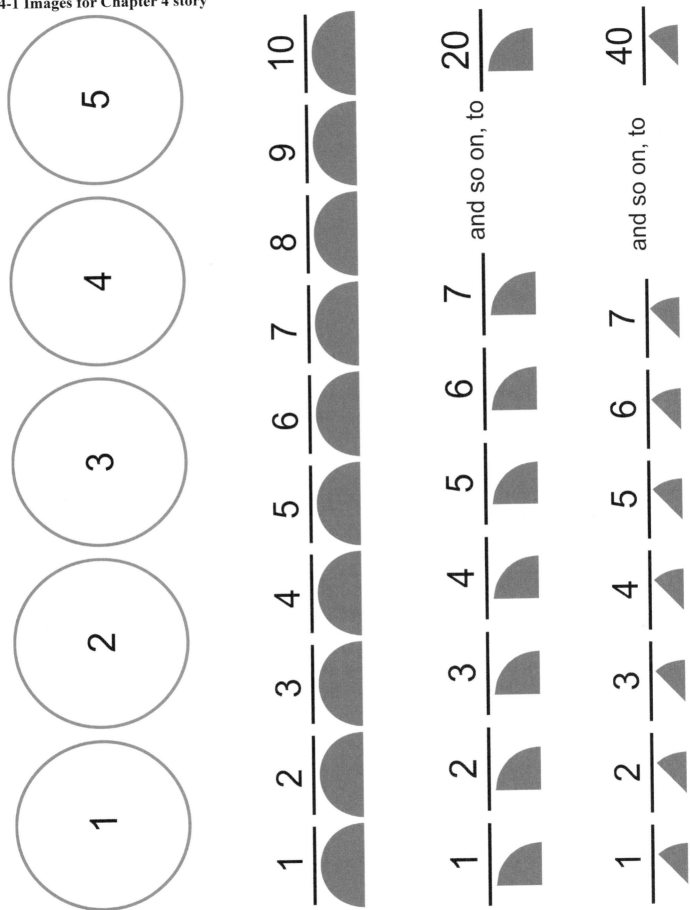

For each model, figure out the fractional part shown, then count the parts. Finally, write the fractions.

1. This one is done for you.

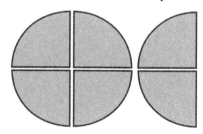

$$\frac{1}{4} \quad \frac{2}{4} \quad \frac{3}{4} \quad \frac{4}{4} \quad \frac{5}{4} \quad \frac{6}{4}$$

2.

3.

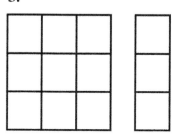

4.

5.

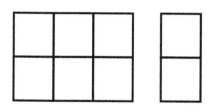

6.

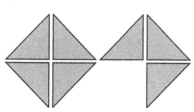

7.

8.

4-3 Share a pizza with friends

Cut out the circles below. Fold each circle to show sharing a pizza between 8 children, then 12, then 4, and finally between 6 children.

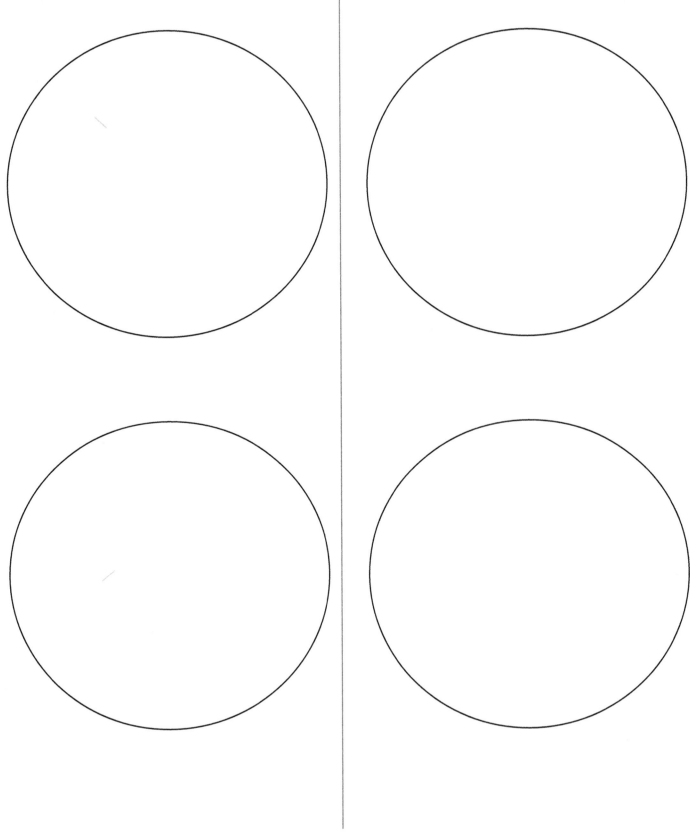

Name_____

Use these models as you answer questions about
comparing fractional parts.

1.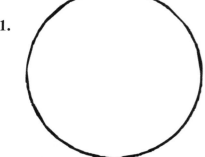

2.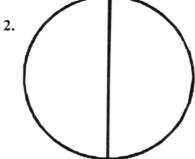

3.

4.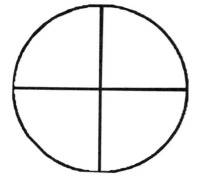

5.

6.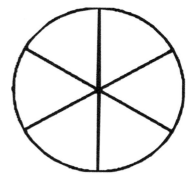

7.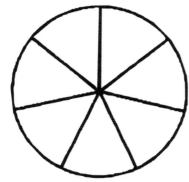

8.

9.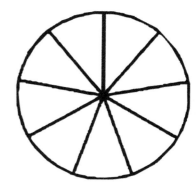

10.

11.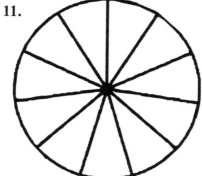

12.

For each question below, circle the fraction that is
the correct answer to the question.

1. Which is bigger?

$$\frac{1}{9} \qquad \frac{1}{5}$$

2. Which is bigger?

$$\frac{1}{3} \qquad \frac{1}{4}$$

3. Which is bigger?

$$\frac{2}{3} \qquad \frac{2}{4}$$

4. Which is bigger?

$$\frac{2}{11} \qquad \frac{2}{7}$$

5. Which is bigger?

$$\frac{3}{9} \qquad \frac{3}{8}$$

6. Which is bigger?

$$\frac{2}{5} \qquad \frac{2}{7}$$

7. Which is bigger?

$$\frac{1}{8} \qquad \frac{2}{4}$$

8. Which is smaller?

$$\frac{1}{3} \qquad \frac{2}{4}$$

9. Which is smaller?

$$\frac{1}{3} \qquad \frac{1}{11}$$

10. Which is smaller?

$$\frac{2}{8} \qquad \frac{2}{7}$$

11. Which is smaller?

$$\frac{3}{3} \qquad \frac{10}{11}$$

12. Which is smaller?

$$\frac{2}{5} \qquad \frac{2}{10}$$

13. Which is smaller?

$$\frac{1}{8} \qquad \frac{1}{9}$$

14. Which is smaller?

$$\frac{3}{4} \qquad \frac{3}{5}$$

 # IMPROPER FRACTIONS

Goals for This Chapter:

1. Review counting fractional parts for more than one whole
2. Practice writing improper fractions
3. Learn to assemble a whole from fractional parts
4. Learn what a fraction for a whole looks like

I. Counting and writing improper fractions

Give students a copy of Resource 5-1 to use as you tell this story. They will answer questions as you go.

NUM and NOM had just finished baking and cutting 3 large pizzas into 8 pieces each. You can see them in example 1. Let's write a fraction for the three pizzas.

1.

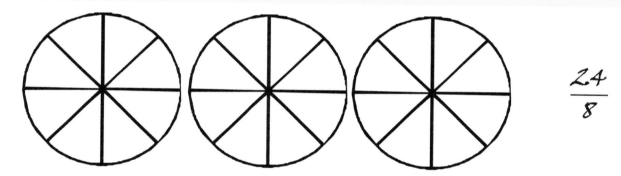

$$\frac{24}{8}$$

Just then, a huge dog ran through the kitchen chasing after a yowling cat. The cat jumped onto the table and of course the dog followed, knocking some pieces to the floor! The dog stopped long enough to gulp down the pieces that fell on the floor before running off after the cat.

Now this is what the pizza on the table looks like:

2.

$$\frac{12}{8}$$

Num and Nom were stunned! "We have to find out how much pizza we have left," they said.

We know that the pizzas were cut into eighths, so that makes it easy to count these fractional parts to

see how many there are. On your sheet, count and write a fraction for example 2. Now let's stop the story for a few minutes and look at some other fractional parts. We will count them, and write fractions for them.

3.

Q: What fractional part are we working with? [thirds] Make that part of the fraction [/3]

Q: How many thirds do we have? [5]

Finish the fraction [5/3]

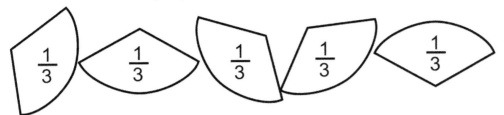

4.

Q: What fractional part are we working with? [fourths] Make that part of the fraction [/4]

Q: How many fourths do we have? [5]

Finish the fraction [5/4]

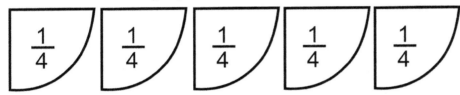

5.

Q: What fractional part are we working with? [sixths] Make that part of the fraction [/6]

Q: How many sixths do we have? [9]

Finish the fraction [9/6]

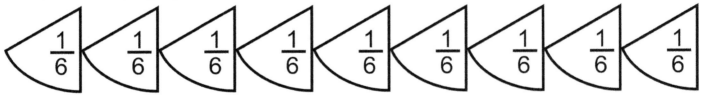

6.

Q: What fractional part are we working with? [ninths] Make that part of the fraction [/9]

Q: How many ninths do we have? [11]

Finish the fraction [11/9]

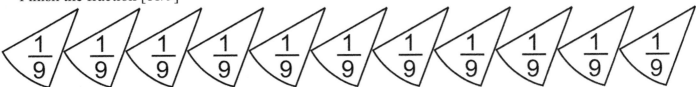

Lets look at each of the fractions we just wrote on our sheets. Here is what we have:

$$\frac{5}{3} \quad \frac{5}{4} \quad \frac{9}{6} \quad \frac{11}{9} \quad \frac{3}{2}$$

Look at these fractions. What is the same about them? [NUM is bigger than NOM]

Fractions like these are called **improper fractions**. Something improper is something we shouldn't do, like shoving people, yelling in the house, or burping loudly in a restaurant. Those things aren't proper.

Improper fractions are fractions where the top number is larger than the bottom number, which means that there are more fractional parts than we need to make one whole. The reason this is improper is because *fractions are supposed to be parts of a whole, not more than a whole*. Show students the image on page 57.

II. Fractions for wholes

Give students Resource 5-2. NUM and NOM began to reassemble the pizzas in their pans. They started by putting pieces of pizza back into the first pan until it was full.

It looked like this (see example 1 on Resource 5-2):

1. Q: How many whole pizzas do they have so far? [1] Let's write a fraction for the whole pizza.

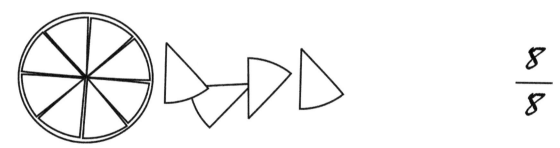

$$\frac{8}{8}$$

Next, they gathered the rest of the pieces into another pizza pan. It looked like this:

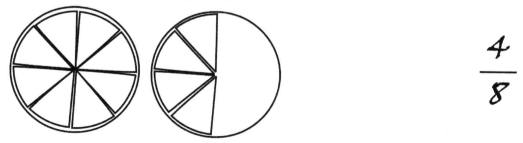

$$\frac{4}{8}$$

2. Q: How many pieces are left over in the second pan? [4] Write a fraction for the second pan. [4/8]

3. Q: What is the fraction for both pans together? Let's talk about it. If you write a fraction for all the eighths that are left, it would start out like this /8 because we are counting eighths. We would start with the whole pizza first [1, 2, 3, 4, 5, 6, 7, 8] and then continue to the second pan [9, 10, 11, 12]: We'd have 12/8.

We can make an equation and it will look like this:

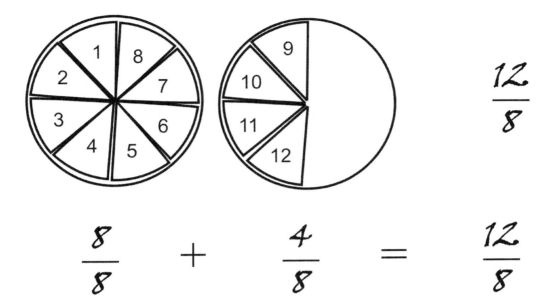

$$\frac{8}{8} \quad + \quad \frac{4}{8} \quad = \quad \frac{12}{8}$$

Hands On:
Use Resource 5-3 Counting fractional parts for a "whole and more."

Next we will practice writing fractions for a whole and also for the additional fractional parts. Students will name the fractional part, count how many parts there are in the whole, write a fraction for the whole, and finally will write a fraction for the remaining parts.

Hands On:
Use Resource 5-4 Wholes and their fractions.

In the next exercise, students will have blank models and improper fractions provided. They will need to color the models to reflect the improper fractions provided. In the next exercise, students will match improper fractions to blank models and then color the correct number of fractional parts.

Hands On:
Use Resource 5-5 Coloring models to reflect improper fractions.

Hands On:
Use Resource 5-6 Linking improper fractions to their models.

Use Resource 5-7 What I know about improper fractions, to determine what your students understand and where they might need more practice. In this assessment, Part 1 will have them writing a fraction for a whole, another for the remaining parts, and then writing an improper fraction for the whole model. Part 2 will have them coloring blank models to match the improper fraction provided. Part 3 will have students identifying improper fractions from a selection provided them, while in Part 4, they will be circling fractions that represent "wholes."

An Improper Fraction
Num is larger than Nom. Num is yelling and shoving, which is improper.

5-1 Counting fractional parts

Name_____

Count the fractional parts and then write the fraction for each example.

1.

2.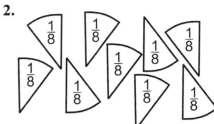

3.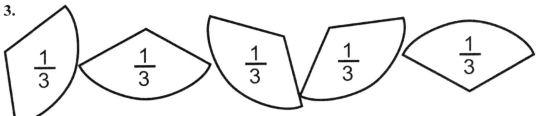

4.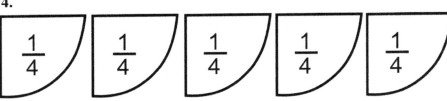

5.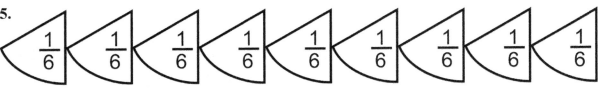

6.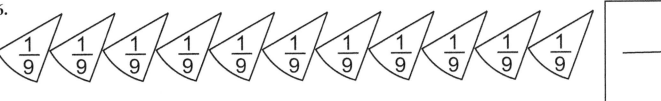

58

3.

2.

1.

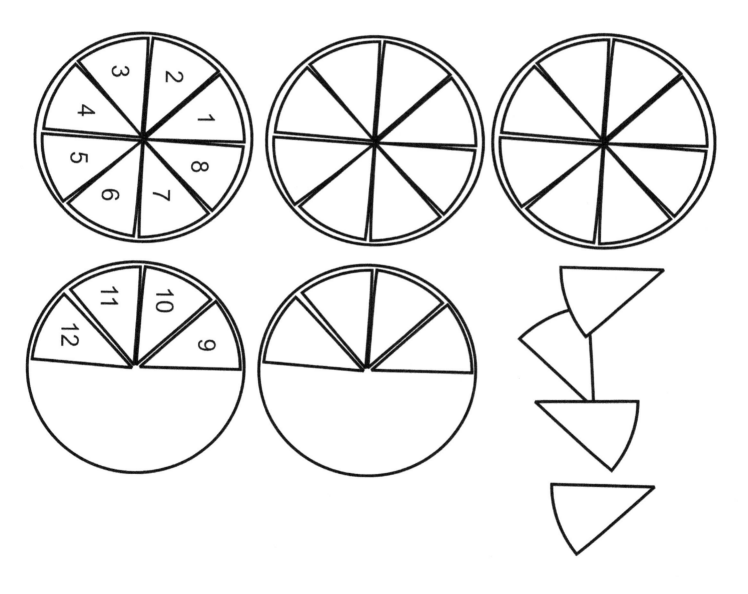

1.

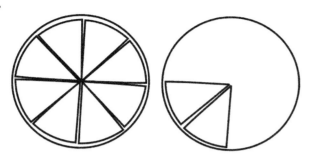

a. Name fractional part:_____

b. How many parts are there?_____

c. Write the improper fraction: _____

2.

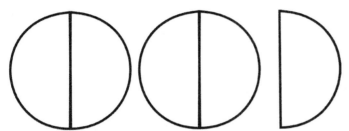

a. Name fractional part:_____

b. How many parts are there?_____

c. Write the improper fraction: _____

3.

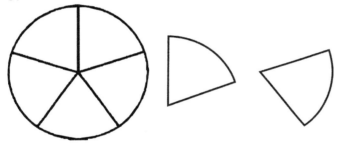

a. Name fractional part:_____

b. How many parts are there?_____

c. Write the improper fraction: _____

4.

a. Name fractional part:_____

b. How many parts are there?_____

c. Write the improper fraction: _____

5.

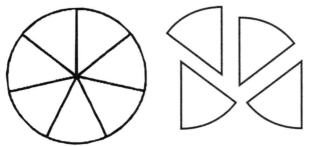

a. Name fractional part:_____

b. How many parts are there?_____

c. Write the improper fraction: _____

5-4 Wholes and their fractions

Name_____

1.

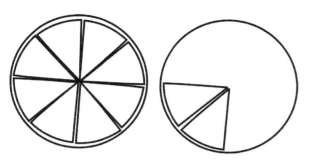

a. Name fractional part:_____

b. How many parts are in the whole? _____

c. Write a fraction for the whole: _____

d. Write a fraction for the rest: _____

2.

a. Name fractional part:_____

b. How many parts are in the whole? _____

c. Write a fraction for the whole: _____

d. Write a fraction for the rest: _____

3.

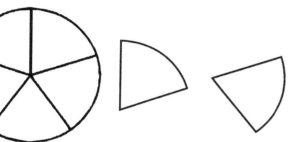

a. Name fractional part:_____

b. How many parts are in the whole? _____

c. Write a fraction for the whole: _____

d. Write a fraction for the rest: _____

4.

a. Name fractional part:_____

b. How many parts are in the whole? _____

c. Write a fraction for the whole: _____

d. Write a fraction for the rest: _____

5.

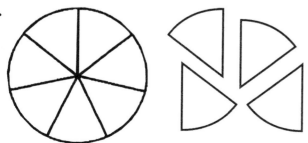

a. Name fractional part:_____

b. How many parts are in the whole? _____

c. Write a fraction for the whole: _____

d. Write a fraction for the rest: _____

5-5 Coloring models to reflect improper fractions   **Name**_____

In each of the models below, the top row represents one whole. Find the fractional part represented in the whole, then color in the number of parts to match the improper fraction given:

1.

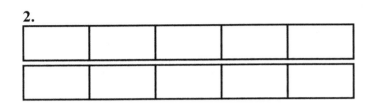

Color the model to show this improper fraction:

$$\frac{5}{4}$$

2.

Color the model to show this improper fraction:

$$\frac{7}{5}$$

3.

Color the model to show this improper fraction:

$$\frac{8}{6}$$

4.

Color the model to show this improper fraction:

$$\frac{11}{7}$$

5.

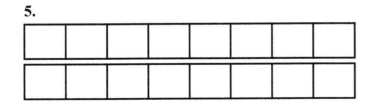

Color the model to show this improper fraction:

$$\frac{12}{8}$$

For each of these improper fractions, find the model that shows the correct denominator, write the fraction by it, then color in the correct number of fractional parts.

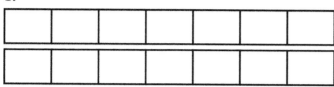

$$\frac{6}{4} \qquad \frac{9}{5} \qquad \frac{11}{6} \qquad \frac{13}{7} \qquad \frac{10}{8}$$

1.

2.

3.

4.

5.

5-7 What I know about improper fractions

Name_____

Part 1:

Write an improper fraction for each model by each picture.

1.

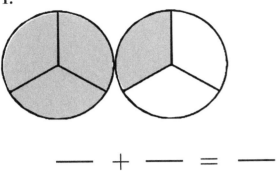

— + — = —

2.

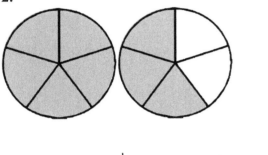

— + — = —

3.

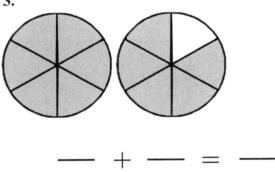

— + — = —

4.

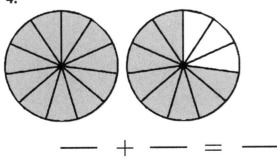

— + — = —

Part 2:

Color in the correct number of fractional parts to match each improper fraction.

5.

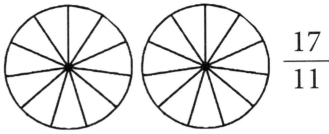

$\dfrac{17}{11}$

6.

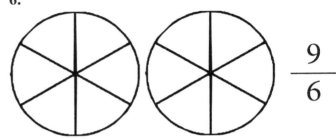

$\dfrac{9}{6}$

7.

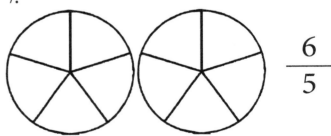

$\dfrac{6}{5}$

8.

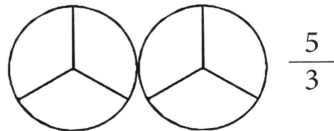

$\dfrac{5}{3}$

Part 3:

Circle all the improper fractions below:

9. $\dfrac{8}{11}$

10. $\dfrac{6}{4}$

11. $\dfrac{17}{11}$

12. $\dfrac{9}{6}$

13. $\dfrac{3}{4}$

14. $\dfrac{2}{6}$

15. $\dfrac{7}{5}$

16. $\dfrac{12}{10}$

17. $\dfrac{5}{3}$

Part 4:

BONUS! Look at the fractions below and see if you can find "wholes." Circle them.

18. $\dfrac{8}{5}$

19. $\dfrac{6}{5}$

20. $\dfrac{11}{11}$

21. $\dfrac{9}{6}$

22. $\dfrac{4}{4}$

23. $\dfrac{6}{6}$

24. $\dfrac{6}{5}$

25. $\dfrac{5}{3}$

26. $\dfrac{5}{5}$

MIXED NUMBERS

Goals for This Chapter:

1. Learn the term "mixed number" and understand what it means
2. Learn to change a fraction for a "whole" to a whole number
3. Learn to change improper fractions to mixed numbers
4. Learn to change mixed numbers to improper fractions

I. Breaking down improper fractions:

Let's review the pizza story from Chapter 5.

Num and Nom had just finished baking and cutting 3 large pizzas into 8 pieces each. Here they are:

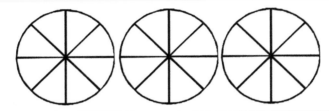

Just then, a huge dog ran through the kitchen chasing after a yowling cat. The cat jumped onto the table and of course the dog followed! The dog stopped long enough to eat the pieces that fell on the floor before running off after the cat again. Now this is what the pizza on the table looks like:

The only way the brothers knew to find out how much pizza was left was to reassemble the pizzas in their pans. So they started putting pieces of pizza back into the first pan until it was full. Let's write one fraction for the whole pizza and another one for the slices that are left over:

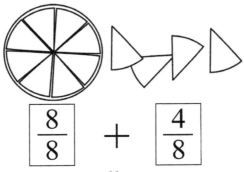

Let's write fractions for new models:

A. This is what the whole looks like: These are the parts we are working with:

 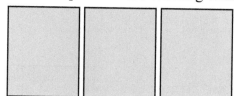

First we fill the whole with as many parts as will fit, and then we see what is left over:

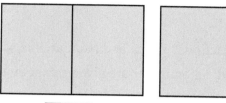

Now let's write fractions for each. $\frac{2}{2}$ + $\frac{1}{2}$ Two pieces fit into the whole, so we
know we are working with halves.

B. This is the whole: These are the parts we are working with:

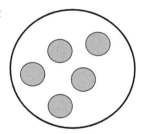 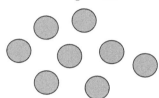

Let's make a whole set first:

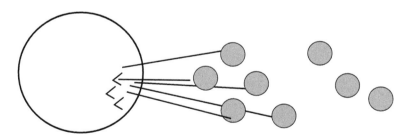

We now have a set and three left over. Let's write the fractions for these. Resource 6-1 shows models of mixed numbers for all three types of wholes: area, length, and set.

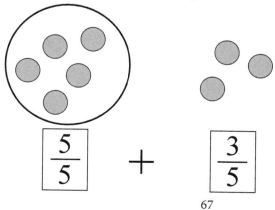

$\frac{5}{5}$ + $\frac{3}{5}$

67

II. Changing a fraction for a whole into a whole number:

Let's look at the models we just worked with:

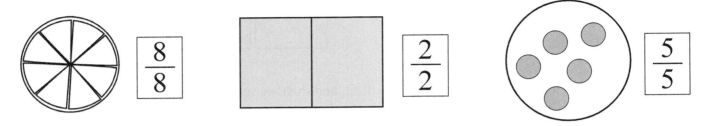

Q. What is the same about these three fractions? [Num and Nom are the same in each]. This is the pattern for fractions for wholes. The numerator and denominator are always exactly the same number.

Q. Is there a shortcut way of showing a whole other than writing a fraction like we did here? Let the children think and discuss and see who comes up with just using the number 1 for 1 whole.

Say, "When we have 8 eighths, 2 halves, 5 fifths, 4 fourths, 9 ninths, etc., we really just have one whole. So the shortcut for writing 1 whole is just to write '1.'"

Next, let's simplify:

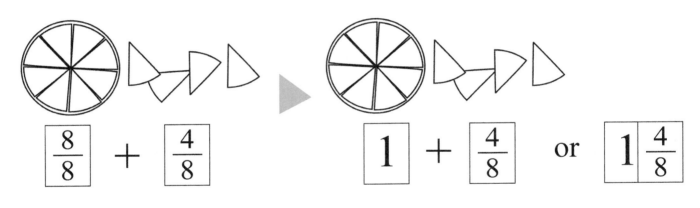

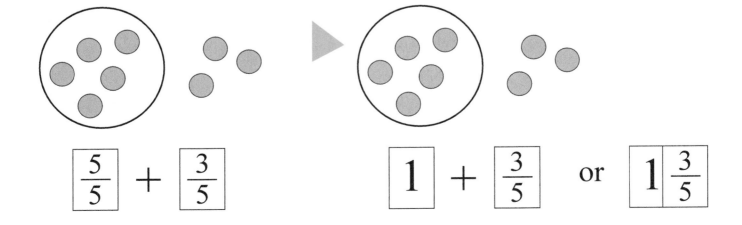

Here is a visual you can share with your students of a mixed number. Actually, Mr. 1 is looking mixed up himself! He is not used to standing beside a fraction, but I am sure he will settle down eventually!

MIXED NUMBER

Whole numbers and fractions together are called "mixed numbers." They are mixed because they are not the same. Look at the example below. The Venn Diagram shows what happens when we combine two different types of numbers.

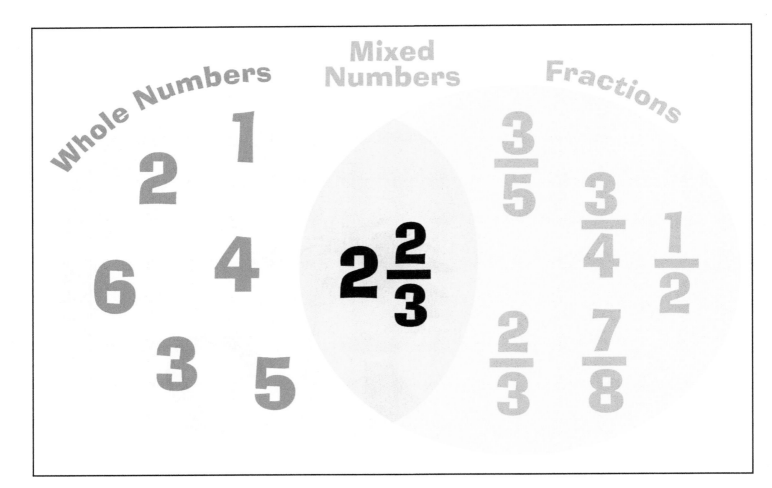

III. Becoming all proper - practice writing mixed numbers

Give students Resource 6-2 so they have the same graphics you have as you work through these examples together.

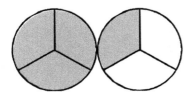

1.

Q: How many thirds do we need to make a whole? [3]

Q: What is the fraction for the whole? [3/3]

Q: Can you change the fraction into a whole number? [1]

Q: How many thirds are left over? [1]

Write a fraction for the leftovers. [1/3]

Put the two numbers side by side: [1 whole plus 1/3 more].

Make it simple: [1 1/3]

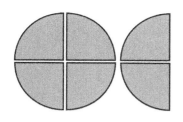

2.

Q: How many fourths do we need to make a whole? [4]

Q: What is the fraction for the whole? [4/4]

Q: Can you change the fraction into a whole number? [1]

Q: How many fourths are left over? [2]

Write that fraction [2/4]

Now combine the fractions [1 2/4]

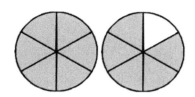

3.

Q: How many sixths do we need to make a whole? [6]

Q: What is the fraction for the whole? [6/6]

Q: Can you change the fraction into a whole number? [1]

Q: How many sixths are leftover? [5]

Write the fraction [5/6]

Now combine the fractions and simplify [1 5/6]

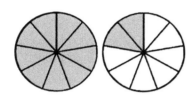

4.

Q: How many ninths do we need to make a whole? [9]

Q: What is the fraction for the whole? [9/9]

Q: Can you change the fraction into a whole number? [1]

Q: How many ninths are leftover? [2]

Write that fraction [2/9]

Now combine the fractions and simplify [1 2/9]

Hands On:

Use Resource 6-3 Writing mixed numbers from models.

IV. Practice changing improper fractions to mixed numbers

Hand out Resource 6-4. Do a few of the problems together, then let the children finish the activity. Encourage the students to draw models for themselves if they need to before they transition to using just numbers. It is important for them to see and understand what they are doing, rather than just memorizing procedures.

1. 4/3. Write the improper fraction on the whiteboard.

Q: What is the fractional part? [thirds]

Q: How many do we need in order to make a whole? [3] Write the whole [1]

Q: How many thirds are left? [1] Write the fraction by the 1 [1 1/3]

2. 13/8

Q: What is the fractional part? [eighths]

Q: How many eighths make a whole? [8] Write the whole [1]

Q: How many are left? [5] Write the fraction by the 1 [5/8]

Hands On:
Use Resource 6-4 Changing improper fractions to mixed numbers.

V. Changing mixed numbers to improper fractions

Believe it or not, sometimes you will NEED to be improper! This will be especially important when your students begin to add and subtract fractions. Let's practice turning mixed numbers into improper fractions.

Remember the story of Num and Nom and the dog chasing the cat? Num and Nom had to figure out how much pizza was left after the dog ate several pieces. The brothers had a couple of friends coming over for dinner and they wanted to figure out how many slices each person would get. They decided to count the individual slices and then they came up with this improper fraction: 12/8.

Do these three problems together before giving the students Resource 6-5 to complete independently.

1. Let's use 1 2/3

Q: We have one whole. How many thirds is that? [3] So the fraction for the whole is 3/3.

Q: If we have 3 thirds and 2 thirds more, how many thirds in all? [5/3]. So 1 2/3 = 5/3 in all.

2. Let's use 2 1/2

Q: We have 2 wholes. How many halves are in 2 wholes? [4] So the fraction for 2 wholes is 4/2.

Q: If we have 4 halves and 1 half, how many halves in all? [5/2]

3. Let's use 1 3/9

Q: We have 1 whole. How many ninths are in 1 whole? [9] So the fraction for the whole is 9/9.

Q: If we have 9 ninths and 3 ninths, how many ninths in all? [12/9]

Finish this chapter by using Resource 6-6 to test the students' understanding of mixed numbers.

Hands On:
Use Resource 6-5 Changing mixed numbers to improper fractions.

Area

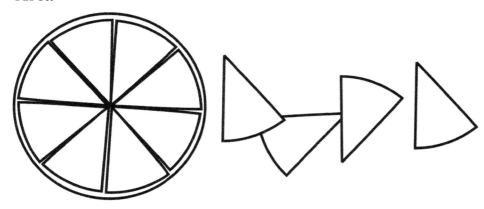

Length

Set

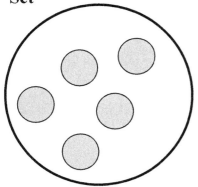

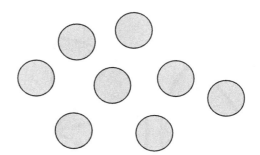

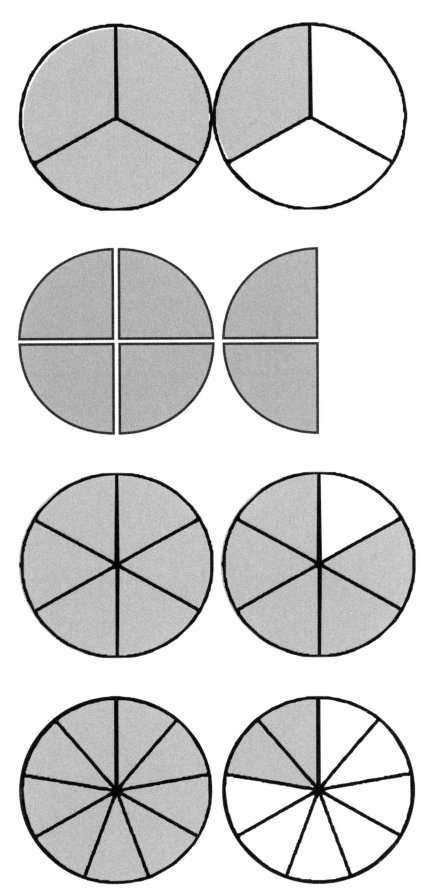

6-3 Writing mixed numbers from models

First figure out the fractional part, next write a number for the whole and finish by writing the fraction for the fractional parts.

1.

2.

3.

4.

5.

6-4 Changing improper fractions to mixed numbers

Name_____

For each of the improper fractions below, first take out enough fractional parts to make a whole [1], then finish the mixed number by writing a fraction for the fractional parts that are left over. The first one is done for you.

1. $\dfrac{7}{5}$ $\dfrac{7}{5} - \dfrac{5}{5} = \dfrac{2}{5}$

   1 whole

   $\boxed{1\frac{2}{5}}$

2. $\dfrac{7}{6}$ $\boxed{}$

3. $\dfrac{7}{4}$ $\boxed{}$

4. $\dfrac{8}{3}$ $\boxed{}$

5. $\dfrac{9}{7}$ $\boxed{}$

6. $\dfrac{13}{8}$ $\boxed{}$

7. $\dfrac{3}{2}$ $\boxed{}$

8. $\dfrac{15}{11}$ $\boxed{}$

9. $\dfrac{13}{10}$ $\boxed{}$

10. $\dfrac{9}{5}$ $\boxed{}$

11. $\dfrac{5}{4}$ $\boxed{}$

12. $\dfrac{9}{6}$ $\boxed{}$

13. $\dfrac{9}{8}$ $\boxed{}$

14. $\dfrac{12}{7}$ $\boxed{}$

15. $\dfrac{16}{9}$ $\boxed{}$

16. $\dfrac{5}{2}$ $\boxed{}$

6-5 Changing mixed numbers to improper fractions

Name_____

For each of the mixed numbers below, first make a fraction for the whole, then add it to the fraction that is already there. This will give you the improper fraction. Remember that in a fraction for a whole, Num and Nom are the same. The first one is done for you.

1. 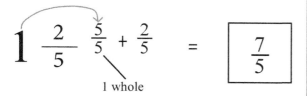 $1 \frac{2}{5}$ $\frac{5}{5} + \frac{2}{5}$ = $\boxed{\frac{7}{5}}$ 1 whole

9. $1 \frac{4}{10}$ $\boxed{}$

2. $1 \frac{1}{6}$ $\boxed{}$

10. $2 \frac{4}{5}$ $\boxed{}$

3. $1 \frac{3}{4}$ $\boxed{}$

11. $2 \frac{1}{4}$ $\boxed{}$

4. $2 \frac{1}{3}$ $\boxed{}$

12. $1 \frac{2}{6}$ $\boxed{}$

5. $1 \frac{5}{7}$ $\boxed{}$

13. $1 \frac{5}{8}$ $\boxed{}$

6. $1 \frac{3}{8}$ $\boxed{}$

14. $1 \frac{2}{7}$ $\boxed{}$

7. $2 \frac{1}{2}$ $\boxed{}$

15. $1 \frac{4}{9}$ $\boxed{}$

8. $1 \frac{3}{11}$ $\boxed{}$

16. $2 \frac{2}{3}$

6-6 What I know about mixed numbers

Name_____

Part 1
Answer the questions below using words and then give examples using numbers.

1. What is an improper fraction?

Examples:

2. What is a mixed number?

Examples:

3. What does a fraction for a whole look like?

Examples:

Part 2
Write a mixed number for each model.

1.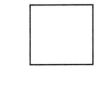

2.

3.

4.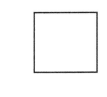

5.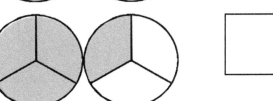

6.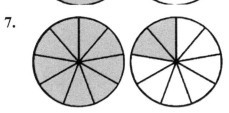

7.

8.

Name_____

Part 3

Change each improper fraction to a
mixed number. Draw a little picture if it
helps you.

9. $\dfrac{12}{9}$

10. $\dfrac{5}{3}$

11. $\dfrac{9}{4}$

12. $\dfrac{8}{6}$

13. $\dfrac{10}{8}$

14. $\dfrac{13}{7}$

15. $\dfrac{12}{5}$

16. $\dfrac{5}{2}$

Part 4

Change each mixed number into an
improper fraction. Draw a little picture if
it helps you.

17. $1\dfrac{3}{5}$

18. $1\dfrac{2}{6}$

19. $1\dfrac{1}{4}$

20. $2\dfrac{2}{3}$

21. $1\dfrac{2}{7}$

22. $1\dfrac{5}{8}$

23. $2\dfrac{1}{2}$

24. $1\dfrac{3}{4}$

7 PRACTICE WITH PARTS & WHOLES

Goals for This Chapter:

1. Review fractions concepts and terms
2. Given the whole, learn to find a specified part
3. Given the part, learn to find the whole
4. Given the improper fraction, learn to find the whole
5. Given the improper fraction, learn to find the mixed number

I. Review fraction parts and terms

Let's review what we already know before we enjoy some activities that will deepen our understanding of **wholes** and **parts**.

Num was holding a plate he just dried and suddenly it slipped from his hands and crashed to the floor. Of course the plate was broken! There wasn't a whole plate any longer, just some **fractional parts**. *In fact, one of the five parts got smashed to smithereens and wasn't even a part any longer. So there were only four parts left.*

Remember Num, or **Numerator,** is the guy in charge of **counting** fractional parts. Nom or **Denominator** is in charge of **naming** the parts.

I COUNT the fractional parts we are working with.

When the plate broke into fractional parts, one of which smashed into smithereens, Nom said, "We're counting fifths, Num." And Num immediately began to count, "1 fifth, 2 fifths, 3 fifths, 4 fifths." 4/5 is how much of the plate is left over.

I NAME the fractional part we are working with.

But then Num dropped another plate and it also magically broke into 5 pieces. Nom says, "Well, we're still counting fifths," so Num continued counting, "5 fifths, 6 fifths, 7 fifths, 8 fifths, and 9 fifths. We have 9 fifths in all."

What the brothers have is more than 1 whole plate, so it is an **improper fraction**! *Next, the boys whipped out their glue guns and tried to patch up the plates. They made 1 whole plate and 4 fifths of another one. Now they have 1 4/5 plates. 1 4/5 is a* **mixed number** *- a combination of a whole number and a fraction. (See next page.)*

Now that we have reviewed, let's do some activities together to practice wholes, fractions, and parts.

Here are pictures of Improper Fraction and Mixed Number in case you forgot their faces:

II. Parts, wholes, and fractions

A. Use Resource 7-1 for this section. You will be working through the problems together at first **finding the fraction** to represent the part shown. For each example, say, "If this is the whole, and this is the part, what is the fraction for the part? Answers are in [ ]. Students will first identify the fractional part, next will see how many fractional parts are selected, and then will write the fraction. Let the students complete Resource 7-1 offering support as they might need it.

WHOLES	PARTS	FRACTIONS
1.		$[\ \frac{1}{4}\ ]$
2.		$[\ \frac{2}{6}\ ]$
3.		$[\ \frac{9}{12}\ ]$
4.		$[\ \frac{5}{6}\ ]$

B. In this next activity, we will show the whole and the fraction, and this time our task will be to **show the part** the fraction represents. Use Resource 7-2 and instruct the students to first identify the fractional part (thirds, fourths, etc.), and then check the fraction to see how many fractional parts they need to color.

	WHOLES	PARTS	FRACTIONS
1.			$\dfrac{2}{3}$
2.			$\dfrac{3}{5}$
3.			$\dfrac{4}{9}$

III. Working with improper fractions, draw the model

Use Resource 7-3 and work through the problems together. In this section we will deal with improper fractions; we will supply a model for the whole, ask a question, and the student will **draw a model** to show the answer. It is important to focus attention on **Nom** here because he identifies the whole, which is the basis for every improper fraction. Answers are shown in brackets [ ].

	WHOLE	QUESTION	ANSWER
1.		If there are 6 marbles in a whole set, show what 5/3 looks like. [First, identify 1/3. It is 2 marbles. Then draw 5 pairs of marbles.]	
2.		If there are 8 parts in a whole, show what 15/8 would look like. [8 eighths make a whole, now we need 7 eighths more.]	
3.		If there are 4 parts in the whole, show what 7/4 would look like. [4 fourths make a whole, so we need 3 more fourths].	

IV. Given the part, find the whole

Use Resource 7-4 for this section. In this section, we will supply a model of the part, will supply a fraction, and the students will **draw a model of the whole** based on those pieces of information. Work the first few together and then let the students complete the Resource. Answers are in [ ]. Reinforce what a fraction for a whole looks like: 6/6 or 3/3, etc.

PART	FRACTION	WHOLE
1.	The part shown represents 1/3 of the whole. Find the whole.	[ ]
2.	This part represents 1/4. Find the whole.	[ ]
3.	This part represents 1/6. Find the whole.	[ ]
4.	This represents 2/3. Find the whole.	[ ]

V. Given the improper fraction, find the whole

Use Resource 7-5 for this section. In this activity, students will be given models of improper fractions and they will need to determine which part of the model is the **whole**. Answers are in [ ].

MODEL of IMPROPER FRACTION	IMPROPER FRACTION	circle the WHOLE
1.	The improper fraction is 5/4. [Each square is one fourth. How many fourths make a whole? 4.] Circle the whole.	[ ]
2.	The improper fraction is 5/3. [Each square is a third. How many thirds are there in a whole? 3.] Circle the whole.	[ ]
3.	The improper fraction is 5/2. [Each pair of dots is a half. How many pairs of dots in a whole? 2.] Circle the whole.	[ ]

83

VI. Given the improper fraction, find the mixed number

Use Resource 7-6 for this section. In this activity, instead of just finding the whole, we are also going to create a mixed number. So the students will be given a model for an improper fraction, they will **identify the whole** and then will **write the mixed number**. Answers are in [ ].

	IMPROPER FRACTION	FRACTION	WHOLE	MIXED NUMBER
1.		5/4 Each square is a fourth. 4/4 is the whole.		[1 1/4]
2.		5/3 Each square is a third. 3/3 is the whole.		[1 2/3]
3.		5/2 Each pair of dots is a half. 2 pairs = a whole.		[2 1/2]

VI. Practice with whole, part, and fraction

Use Resource 7-7 for this section. We are going to mix up what we are asking for. Sometimes we will be asking for the whole, sometimes the part, and sometimes the fraction. Answers are in [ ].

	WHOLE	PART	FRACTION
1.		This part is 1/2 of the whole.	1/2
2.	What is 1/4 of this model?	[ ]	1/4
3.		What part of the whole is this part?	[1/4]

VII. Hands-on activities with math chips

Every child will need some math counters. For each problem, they will consult with Num (how many) and Nom (of what) as they find the whole. What they start with is the fractional part and they will be looking for the whole.

WHAT YOU HAVE	THE FRACTION	THE WHOLE
1. You have 1 chip.	1 chips = 1/3. What is the whole?	[How many **more** chips = a whole? 2 How many chips in a whole? 3]
2. You have 1 chip.	1 chips = 1/4. What is the whole?	[How many **more** chips = a whole? 3 How many chips in a whole? 4.]
3. You have 1 chip.	1 chips = 1/5. What is the whole?	[How many **more** chips = a whole? 4 How many chips in a whole? 5 chips.]
4, You have 2 chips.	2 chips = 1/3. What is the whole?	[How many **more** pairs = a whole? 2 How many chips in a whole? 6]
5. You have 3 chip.	3 chips = 1/2. What is the whole?	[How many more threes = a whole?1 How many chips in a whole? 6.]
6. You have 2 chips.	2 chips = 1/4. What is the whole?	[How many fourths in a whole? 4 [How many chips in a whole? 8.]

If the children are comfortable with this exercise, go on to the next section in which they will use graph paper to work out the problems.

VII. Hands-on activities with graph paper

Give your students graph paper and pencils. See Resource 7-8. They will follow your directions as they work out each problem. The blue outline completes the whole in examples 1-2 or shows the whole in 3-5. The third column here shows the answers to the problems

DRAW AROUND ___ SQUARES	SAY:	WHOLE
1.	Outline 2 squares. If these two squares = 1/6. What is the whole? [1/6 is 2 squares. How many more pairs of squares are in 6/6? 5 more pairs.]	
2.	Outline 4 squares. These four squares = 2/3. How many squares are in just 1/3? [2]. [We have 2 thirds, but we need 3 thirds. How many squares are in 3/3? 6.] What is the whole?	

DRAW AROUND ___ SQUARES	SAY:	WHOLE
3.	Outline 10 squares. These 10 squares = 5/3. What is the whole? [How many squares in 1/3? 2. There are 5 sets of 2 squares. How many squares are in 3/3? 9.]	
4.	Outline 5 squares. These 5 squares = 2 1/2. What is the whole? [How many halves in 2 1/2? 5. How many squares = 1/2? [1] How many squares in a whole? [2]	
5.	Outline 6 squares. These 6 squares = 1 1/2. What is the whole? [How many halves in 1 1/2? 3. How many squares in 1/2? [2] How many squares in a whole? [4]	

You will know by this time how comfortable your students are with wholes, fractions, and parts. If you feel it is time to move on, give them the assessment for this chapter. See Resource 7-9.

7-1 Given a whole and a part, write a fraction for the part   Name_____

WHOLE	PART	FRACTION
1.		
2.		
3.		
4.		
5.		
6.		
7.		
8.		

7-2 Given a whole and a fraction, draw the part   Name_____

This is the WHOLE	Color the PART to match the fraction	FRACTION
1.		$\dfrac{2}{3}$
2.		$\dfrac{3}{5}$
3.		$\dfrac{4}{9}$
4.		$\dfrac{5}{6}$
5.		$\dfrac{1}{3}$
6.		$\dfrac{2}{3}$
7.		$\dfrac{7}{8}$
8.		$\dfrac{5}{8}$

WHOLE	FRACTION	Draw a MODEL for the improper fraction
1.	$\dfrac{5}{3}$	
2.	$\dfrac{15}{8}$	
3.	$\dfrac{7}{4}$	
4.	$\dfrac{12}{9}$	
5.	$\dfrac{3}{2}$	
6.	$\dfrac{4}{3}$	
7.	$\dfrac{7}{3}$	
8.	$\dfrac{9}{6}$	

7-4 Given the part and fraction, find the whole   Name_____

PART	FRACTION	Draw a MODEL for the WHOLE
1. ○	$\dfrac{1}{3}$	
2. △	$\dfrac{1}{4}$	
3. ▢	$\dfrac{1}{6}$	
4. ⬡⬡	$\dfrac{2}{3}$	
5. ▭▭▭	$\dfrac{3}{5}$	
6. ⬡⬡⬡	$\dfrac{3}{7}$	
7. △△△ △△	$\dfrac{5}{8}$	
8. ⊞	$\dfrac{4}{6}$	

7-5 Given the improper fraction, find the whole

Name_____

MODEL FOR IMPROPER FRACTION	FRACTION	COLOR THE WHOLE
1.	$\dfrac{5}{4}$	
2.	$\dfrac{5}{3}$	
3.	$\dfrac{5}{2}$	
4.	$\dfrac{8}{6}$	
5.	$\dfrac{5}{4}$	
6.	$\dfrac{3}{2}$	
7.	$\dfrac{9}{5}$	
8.	$\dfrac{9}{6}$	

MODEL OF IMPROPER FRACTION	FRACTION	COLOR THE WHOLE	MIXED NUMBER
1.	$\dfrac{5}{4}$		
2.	$\dfrac{5}{3}$		
3.	$\dfrac{5}{2}$		
4.	$\dfrac{8}{6}$		
5.	$\dfrac{5}{4}$		
6.	$\dfrac{3}{2}$		
7.	$\dfrac{9}{5}$		
8.	$\dfrac{9}{6}$		

WHOLE	PART	FRACTION
1.	○ ○ ○ ○	$\dfrac{1}{2}$
2. △△△△ △△△△		$\dfrac{1}{4}$
3. (square divided in 4)	☐	
4.	○○ ○○ ○○ ○○	$\dfrac{2}{3}$
5. (circle with 5 triangles)	△	
6. (oval with 7 circles)		$\dfrac{2}{6}$
7.	(3 hexagons)	$\dfrac{3}{5}$
8. ○ ○ ○ ○ ○ ○ ○ ○		$\dfrac{5}{8}$

1.

2.

3.

4.

5.

1.

2.

3.

4.

5.

In this table, you will be given a whole and a part. You will write a fraction for each one.

WHOLE	PART	FRACTION
1.		
2.		
3.		

In this table, you will be given a whole and a fraction. Please color the part.

WHOLE	FRACTION	COLOR THE PART
4.	$\dfrac{3}{10}$	
5.	$\dfrac{5}{8}$	
6.	$\dfrac{3}{5}$	

7-9 What I know about whole, part, and fraction, p. 2   Name_____

In this table you will see a model of a whole, an improper fraction, and you will draw a model for the improper fraction.

This is the WHOLE	the IMPROPER FRACTION	MODEL OF IMPROPER FRACTION
1.	$\dfrac{9}{5}$	
2.	$\dfrac{7}{3}$	
3.	$\dfrac{5}{4}$	

In this table you will be given the part and a fraction. You will find the whole and draw it.

PART	FRACTION	DRAW a model for the WHOLE
4.	$\dfrac{1}{4}$	
5.	$\dfrac{1}{6}$	
6.	$\dfrac{3}{5}$	

In this table you will be shown the improper fraction, you will see the improper fraction, and you will color the whole.

IMPROPER FRACTION MODEL	IMPROPER FRACTION	COLOR THE WHOLE
1.	$\dfrac{4}{3}$ How many / Of what	
2.	$\dfrac{3}{2}$	
3.	$\dfrac{6}{4}$	

In this table, you will complete the missing piece: whole, fraction, or part.

WHOLE	FRACTION	PART
4.	$\dfrac{7}{10}$	
5.		
6.	$\dfrac{3}{5}$	

FRACTION NUMBER SENSE

Goals for This Chapter:

1. Learn to compare two fractions to determine which is larger
2. Learn to compare two fractions to determine which is closer to zero
3. Learn to compare two fractions to determine which is closer to 1
4. Learn to compare two fractions to determine which is closer to 1 half
5. Learn to estimate using fractions

I. Two big ideas

If students have good fraction number sense it will make computation with fractions so much easier. They won't just have to memorize the rules for how to add, subtract, multiply or divide, and they will be far more likely to be able to use fractions in their daily lives. By the time students begin the study of fractions, they will have developed number sense for whole numbers and this is the very thing that causes problems for them as they study fractions. For instance, the bigger the number, the more you have, right? Nope, not when you are dealing with fractions! So in this chapter we are going to engage in activities that will help students develop fraction number sense, which will stand them in good stead when we get to computing with fractions.

The big ideas for this chapter and what we want our students to understand instinctively are that:

1. **The denominator** tells how many pieces the whole was cut into, so the bigger Nom is, the smaller the shares will be.

2. **The numerator** will be the key that reveals if a fraction is closer to zero, to 1/2, or to 1. One fractional part will appear to the left, closer to zero, while larger Nums will appear to the right, closer to 1.

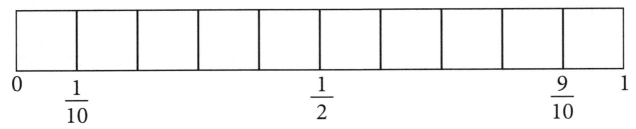

In this example, it is easy to see that 1/10 is very close to zero, while 9/10 is very close to 1.

These are the two big ideas from which all activities in this chapter will flow.

II. Which fraction is bigger

This concept relates to our first big idea, that the larger Nom is, the smaller the share will be. Show the students the following fractions and ask them to identify the larger of the two:

$$\frac{1}{4} \qquad \frac{1}{8}$$

Let the students discuss and offer their opinions. Ask them to share their reasoning with the group. If they quickly select the correct fraction, great, if not, just go on to the hands-on activity.

Hands On:

Use Resource 8-1 Squares to fold.

Ask the children to cut the squares apart. Have them take the first square and fold it in half and then fold it in half again. Next, they will unfold the paper and write 1/4 in each of the four spaces.

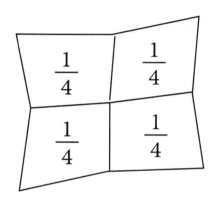

Next, take another square and fold it just like the first one, but this time, fold one more time. Three folds in all. Unfold the paper and write 1/8 in each of the eight spaces on the paper.

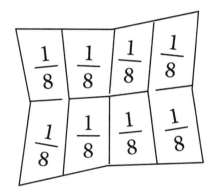

Ask again, "Which is bigger? 1/4 or 1/8?" Ask the children to express why the spaces with the larger denominators are actually smaller than the spaces with the smaller denominators. We trust they will answer that in order to get 8 areas out of the same size paper, they had to make the parts smaller.

Using the same two folded papers, ask, "Which is larger, 3/4 or 3/8?" Let the students color 3/4 and 3/8 if they would like to in order to make each area stand out visually for comparison. Of course the larger area is 3/4. Which is larger, 2/4 or 5/8? [5/8] How about 3/4 or 5/8? [3/4]

Hands On:

Give students Resource 8-2 and ask them to write a fraction in every space on each strip, from the 1 whole at the top to the twelfths at the bottom.

II. Closer to zero, 1 half, or one

We will be doing some hands-on comparing of fractions in this section. Ask the students to take out their fraction strip sheet and cut the strips apart. Have them find the strip that is labeled 1/2 and write a zero to the very left of the strip. To the far right of the strip they will write a 1. In the middle, right on the line they will write 1/2. This is the strip we will use for making comparisons.

For each of the following fractions, ask the students to identify if it is closer to zero, 1/2 or one.

Fraction	Answer		Fraction	Answer
1/3	[1/2]		1/8	[0]
4/5	[1]		3/5	[1/2]
7/8	[1]		6/7	[1]
1/6	[0]		4/7	[1/2]
2/7	[1/2]		2/3	[1/2]

Pause to reflect

Ask the students which is closer to zero: 1/8 or 1/16. They might answer that they don't have a strip for sixteeths. If they do, ask them if they can figure out sixteenth on their eighths strip. What would they need to do to their eighths strip to show sixteenths? [fold each space in half]. Now they can find out which is closer to zero: 1/8 or 1/16. [1/16]

Ask the children to look at the rest of their fraction strips and figure out which new fractions they can make by folding each space in half. [halves ▶ fourths, thirds ▶ sixths, fourths ▶ eighths, fifths ▶ tenths.

Close or Closer?

Use fraction strips again and ask a student to name a fraction he or she feels is very close to 1 whole. When you have an answer, challenge the students to identify a fraction even closer to 1 whole. For example, if the first student chose 15/16 as being the closest to 1 whole, someone could say that 16/17 is even closer to 1 whole because a seventeenth is smaller than a sixteenth. Remember, the larger Dom is, the smaller the piece is. So you could start with 15/16 and progressively get closer to 1: 16/17, 17/18, 18/19, 19/20, etc.

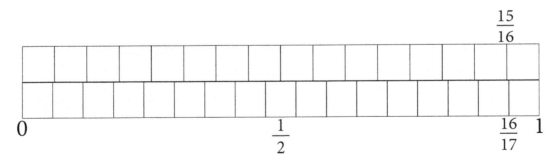

Close to zero

Do this exercise again. This time ask for a fraction that is very close to zero (such as 1/8) and then ask for a fraction even closer to zero. [Possible answers include 1/9, 1/10, 1/11, 1/12, etc.]

Closer to one half

Now let's work with one half. As students consult their strips, ask someone to name a fraction very

close to 1/2. Options may include 1/3, 2/3, 2/5, 3/5, 2/6, 4/6, 3/7, 4/7, etc., or any fraction just to the left or right of the 1/2 line. As before, see if a student can find a fraction even closer to 1/2 than the fraction first suggested. For instance, if someone says 4/10, fractions closer to 1/2 than 4/10 are 5/12 and 6/14. The key to finding a fraction closer to 1/2 is to make Nom larger than 10 (so the fractional part is smaller) and then choose a number for Num that is just to the left or right of the middle. If we use twelfths, we would not use 6/12 because that is right on the half way line. We would choose to use either 5/12 or 7/12s. What are some other options? (6/13 or 7/13, 6/14 or 8/14, etc.). In this example, we will use fourteenths:

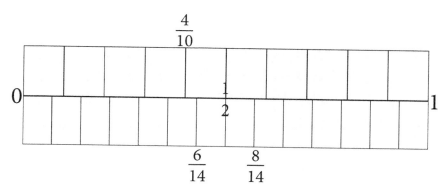

III. Which fraction is more?

Now we are going to just look at pairs of fractions and see if we can use our intuition to guess which fraction is more. The point of this activity is not to arrive at the correct answer as much as it is to talk about relative sizes of fractions and how we can tell which is larger than the other. Let's compare these pairs of fractions together:

	COMPARE	ANSWER			COMPARE	ANSWER
A	4/5 and 4/7	[4/5]		F	5/12 and 7/12	[7/12]
B	3/4 and 3/5	[3/4]		G	3/5 and 3/8	[3/5]
C	4/3 and 5/8	[4/3]		H	5/8 and 6/10	[5/8]
D	3/4 and 9/10	[9/10]		I	9/8 and 4/3	[4/3]
E	3/8 and 4/7	[4/7]		J	1/4 and 3/8	[3/8]

Big ideas to consider when comparing fractions:

1. If Dom is the same in both fractions, just choose the fraction with the larger number of parts (Num). See F in the chart as an example of this idea. 7/12 is obviously going to be bigger than 5/12.

2. If the denominators (Dom) are different but you have the same numerator (Num), the smaller denominator wins because it is the larger fractional part. See B and G in the chart as examples of this idea.

3. Compare the fractions to 1/2 or 1 whole, looking at which is more or less than 1/2 or 1 whole. See E in which 3/8 is smaller than 1/2 and 4/7 is larger than 1/2. See also C in which 4/3 is larger than 1 while 5/8 is smaller than 1.

4. Compare the fractions as to which is closer to 1/2 or 1 whole. See I as an example. Both fractions are more than 1, but 9/8 is closer to 1 whole because the fractional parts are much smaller than thirds. 4/3 would

101

be quite a bit beyond 1 whole in comparison.

Here is the reasoning behind the answers in the table on the previous page:

A. Fifths are larger than sevenths and we have 4 of each.

B. Fourths are larger than fifths and we have the same number of each.

C. 4/3 is larger than 1 whole, while 5/8 is barely larger than 1/2.

D. Even though fourths are larger than tenths, we have 9 tenths which is very close to 1 whole compared to 3/4 which is exactly half way between 1/2 and 1 whole.

E. Sevenths are larger than eighths and we have more sevenths than we do eighths.

F. We are comparing twelfths and 7 of them will be bigger than 5 of them.

G. We have the same number of fractional parts, but fifths are larger than eighths.

H. In this case, 5/8 is just 1/8 larger than 1/2 while 6/10 is 1/10 larger than 1/2. Eighths are larger than tenths, so in this case the eighths win!

I. Comparing to 1 whole, 9/8 and 4/3 are both larger than it, but a third is far larger than a ninth.

J. 3/8 wins because it is exactly 1/8 larger than 1/4.

Hands On:
Use Resource 8-3 Comparing fractions.

IV. Ordering fractions from smallest to largest

Now that we've done a lot of comparisons, let's give the children a tactile activity! Give them Resource 8-4 and have them cut the cards out and then put them in order from smallest to greatest. This is a wonderful activity to do with a partner so the students can discuss their way through the project.

The correct order is: GROUP 1 - 1/10, 1/9, 1/7, 1/5, 1/3, 1/2. GROUP 2 - 1/10, 4/9, 2/3, 3/4, 7/8, 11/12.

V. Estimating Fractions

Now we will be using all our skills from the previous sections in which we were determining if a fraction is closer to 0, to 1/2, or to 1.

1. Ask the children to just guess about how much 15/16 plus 9/10 are. They will answer, "About...." The answer shouldn't be exact of course, but rather a whole number such as "About 1" or "About 2." In this case, both 15/16 and 9/10 are almost 1, and 1+1=2. So 2 should be their estimated answer.

2. **How about 4/5 plus 1/8?** 4/5 is missing 1/5 to be 1 whole. Because 1/8 is a lot smaller than the missing 1/5, the answer is that 4/5 plus 1/8 is "about 1." Have the students check the problem for themselves using fraction strips.

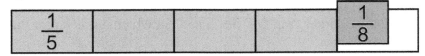

3. **How about 9/10 + 3/8?**

The questions to answer right away are, are the fractions closer to 1/2 or to 1?

In this case, 9/10 is close to 1 while 3/8 is very close to 1/2.

[So the answer should be, "About 1 1/2."]

4. **How about 5/6+2/3?**

5/6 is closest to 1 than to 1/2, but 2/3 is closer to 1/2 than to 1.

[So the answer will be, "About 1 1/2."]

5. **How about 3/7+1/8?**

3/7 is less than 1/2, while 1/8 is closer to 0 than to 1/2.

[The answer is going to be "About 1/2."]

Estimating using mixed numbers:

Let's look at 3 1/8 + 2 4/5.

Ask the students what they would do to begin to estimate the answer. For this problem they will need scratch paper and a pencil to write as they work so they won't forget their thinking.

Hopefully the students will decide to add the whole numbers first: 3+2=5. They will write 5 on their scratch paper. What they need to estimate now is 1/8+4/5.

They will ask themselves which number 1/8 is closest to [0] and then which number 4/5 is closest to [1]. 1+0=1. They will add this 1 to the 5 they wrote on their scratch paper to arrive at an estimated 6.

Hands On:

Work through Resource 8-5 together, assisting the students as they need help. This is a good time for you to let students work with a partner to solve. Remember the point of this excercise is not to arrive at an exact answer, but rather to get the students used to visualizing about how much fractions are. If a child is feeling overwhelmed, encourage him / her to use fraction strips at first, or to sketch the fraction pairs.

Once you feel the students are comfortable with the big ideas in this chapter, give them the assessment - Resource 8-6.

8-1 Squares to fold

8-2 Fraction strips

Write a fraction in every space in each strip below. Next, cut the strips apart.

For each of the following pairs, circle the fraction that is larger. Draw a sketch of the fractions if you need to.

1. $\dfrac{1}{5}$ $\dfrac{1}{9}$ 9. $\dfrac{2}{3}$ $\dfrac{2}{4}$

2. $\dfrac{1}{3}$ $\dfrac{1}{4}$ 10. $\dfrac{1}{6}$ $\dfrac{1}{3}$

3. $\dfrac{1}{6}$ $\dfrac{1}{4}$ 11. $\dfrac{3}{6}$ $\dfrac{2}{3}$

4. $\dfrac{5}{9}$ $\dfrac{5}{6}$ 12. $\dfrac{5}{6}$ $\dfrac{2}{3}$

5. $\dfrac{7}{8}$ $\dfrac{7}{9}$ 13. $\dfrac{2}{8}$ $\dfrac{2}{9}$

6. $\dfrac{1}{7}$ $\dfrac{1}{3}$ 14. $\dfrac{2}{7}$ $\dfrac{1}{3}$

7. $\dfrac{4}{5}$ $\dfrac{4}{9}$ 15. $\dfrac{4}{7}$ $\dfrac{3}{9}$

8. $\dfrac{3}{8}$ $\dfrac{1}{2}$ 16. $\dfrac{5}{8}$ $\dfrac{3}{4}$

8-4 Fraction cards

Name_____

Cut the fraction cards apart. Now put them in order from smallest to largest.

$\dfrac{1}{9}$	$\dfrac{1}{3}$	$\dfrac{1}{5}$
$\dfrac{1}{10}$	$\dfrac{1}{2}$	$\dfrac{1}{7}$

Cut the fraction cards apart. Now put them in order from smallest to largest.

$\dfrac{4}{9}$	$\dfrac{2}{3}$	$\dfrac{3}{4}$
$\dfrac{7}{8}$	$\dfrac{1}{10}$	$\dfrac{11}{12}$

8-5 Estimating fraction sums

For each of the following pairs, estimate the sum. Sketch or make notes as needed in the blank half of the page.

1. $$1\frac{2}{3} + 2\frac{2}{4}$$

2. $$3\frac{1}{3} + 1\frac{1}{6}$$

3. $$2\frac{2}{3} + 3\frac{3}{6}$$

4. $$1\frac{5}{6} + 2\frac{2}{3}$$

5. $$3\frac{2}{8} + 1\frac{2}{9}$$

6. $$2\frac{2}{7} + 3\frac{1}{3}$$

7. $$2\frac{4}{7} + 1\frac{3}{9}$$

8. $$3\frac{5}{8} + 1\frac{3}{4}$$

Name_____

Circle the larger fraction in each pair below.

By each fraction, write whether it is closest to 0, 1/2, or 1.

1. $\dfrac{1}{3}$ $\dfrac{2}{4}$

2. $\dfrac{2}{3}$ $\dfrac{1}{6}$

3. $\dfrac{2}{4}$ $\dfrac{2}{6}$

4. $\dfrac{5}{6}$ $\dfrac{2}{3}$

5. $\dfrac{2}{8}$ $\dfrac{2}{9}$

6. $\dfrac{2}{5}$ $\dfrac{1}{3}$

7. $\dfrac{4}{7}$ $\dfrac{4}{9}$

8. $\dfrac{5}{8}$ $\dfrac{3}{4}$

9. $\dfrac{1}{5}$ _____

10. $\dfrac{5}{6}$ _____

11. $\dfrac{8}{9}$ _____

12. $\dfrac{1}{10}$ _____

13. $\dfrac{3}{8}$ _____

14. $\dfrac{5}{12}$ _____

15. $\dfrac{16}{17}$ _____

16. $\dfrac{2}{13}$ _____

EQUIVALENT FRACTIONS

Goals for This Chapter:

1. Learn what "equivalent" means
2. Learn what equivalent fractions look like in models
3. Learn to create equivalent fractions
4. Explore patterns that exist when we make equivalent fractions
5. Learn how to simplify fractions

I. What equivalent means

If you look in a dictionary for the origins of the word "equivalent," you will get something like this: "Middle English, from Middle French or Late Latin; Middle French, from Late Latin aequivalent-, aequivalens, present participle of aequivalēre to have equal power, from Latin aequi- + valēre to be strong." This is from Webster's Dictionary. Ugh.

Let's do something far more kid-friendly shall we? What I distilled from the formal definition above is that "equi" has to do with being equal or fair, while "valent" is from valiant or strong. So if you put the two together, you get "equally strong." We can go from there to explain that when we say two things are equivalent, they have the same value, but might not be exactly the same in terms of how they are expressed. For instance if you have a T-shirt with a picture of dinosaur on it and your friend borrows it and loses it, he might offer to replace it with a T-shirt with a tiger on the front. It won't be the same T-shirt with the picture of a dinosaur, but it is a T-shirt with an animal on it. A T-shirt to replace the lost T-shirt. Equivalent.

Here is a picture of the word equivalent showing two knights with equal amounts of strength pulling on a rope. They might be there a long time because even though they express themselves differently, they have the same amount of strength. *See larger image of SnapWords® equivalent a couple of pages over.*

© 2014 Sarah Major

We have talked a lot about fractional parts needing to be fair shares. Illustration 1 shows equal or fair shares. Everyone sharing this pizza will have exactly 1/8 of the pizza. In Illustration 2, the two models show equivalent shares. The amount of pizza available in each is the same, but they are not cut the same.

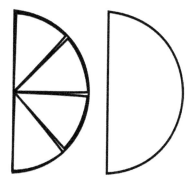

Illustration 1   *Illustration 2*

In Illustration 2, the first portion shows 4/8. The second portion shows 1/2. They have the same amount of pizza in them, but the sizes of the pieces, the fractional parts, are not the same. We can say that 4/8 and 1/2 are equivalent fractions because the amount of pizza available to eat is the same in both of the examples.

II. Models of equivalent fractions

A. Give your students a plain sheet of paper and three different colors of markers or crayons. Say:

1. Fold your paper in half, then fold it in half again as in the illustration.

2. Open the paper and choose a color. Color in 1/4 of the paper and label it with the fraction 1/4.

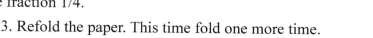

3. Refold the paper. This time fold one more time.

4. Open the paper and using a second color, draw a line over the new fold inside the 1/4 space.

5. Inside the 1/4 space are two new spaces. If you count the spaces in your paper, you will find that the new spaces are 1/8s. Label the two that fall inside the 1/4 area with 1/8.

6. Fold the paper again and once again fold another time.

7. Open the paper and using the third color, mark the lines for the new folds.

8. Write the new fractions (1/16) that fall inside the 1/4 space you colored at the beginning. You will see that 1/4 is equivalent to 2/8 and to 4/16!

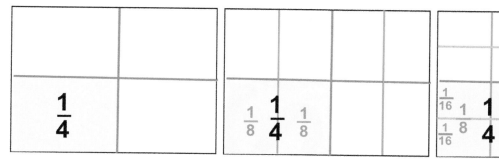

Here is 1/4...   *equivalent to 2/8...*   *and to 4/16.*

111

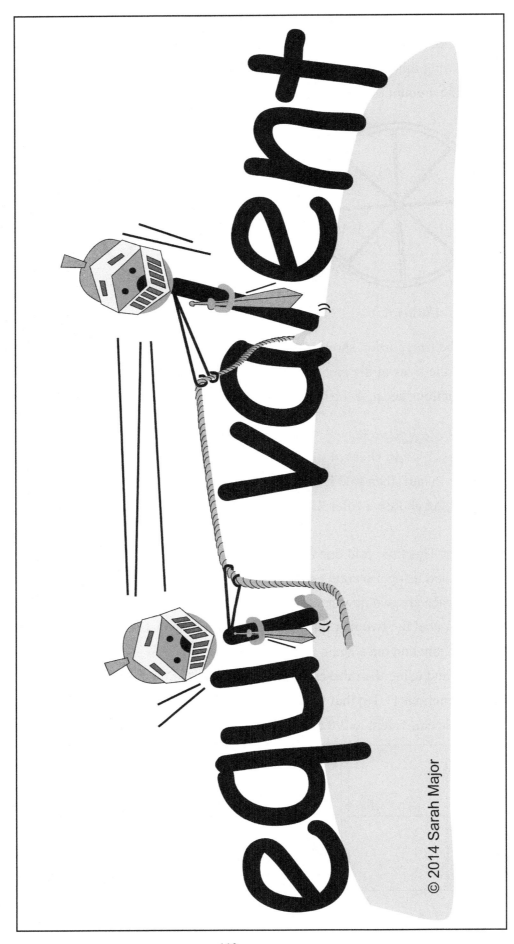

B. Try another example.

Have the students take another sheet of paper, and this time when they fold the paper twice and open it up, they are going to color 3/4 of the paper. The rest of the steps are just like the steps in example 1. This is what their finished product will look like:

$\frac{1}{4}$	$\frac{1}{4}$
$\frac{1}{4}$	

$\frac{1}{8}$	$\frac{1}{8}$	$\frac{1}{8}$	$\frac{1}{8}$
$\frac{1}{8}$	$\frac{1}{8}$		

$\frac{1}{16}$	$\frac{1}{16}$	$\frac{1}{16}$	$\frac{1}{16}$
$\frac{1}{16}$	$\frac{1}{16}$	$\frac{1}{16}$	$\frac{1}{16}$
$\frac{1}{16}$	$\frac{1}{16}$		
$\frac{1}{16}$	$\frac{1}{16}$		

Here is 3/4...   *equivalent to 6/8...*   *and to 12/16.*

If you put the fractions from A. and B. in a row, the students will be able to see a pattern emerging.

$$\frac{1}{4} = \frac{2}{8} = \frac{4}{16} \qquad \frac{3}{4} = \frac{6}{8} = \frac{12}{16}$$

Example A   *Example B*

Hopefully as you study these sequences of fractions, someone will notice that both Num and Nom are doubling as you go towards the right, which reflects the action of folding your paper. See if anyone can verbalize why the numbers are doubling. [Each piece is being divided in half, so there are twice as many sections as before].

C. One more exercise:

If the students still seem a bit uncertain about equivalent fractions, have them fold another sheet of paper once. Open and mark two halves. Color one half lightly.

Have them refold, but this time, they will fold the 1/2 into thirds:

When they open their paper, they will have sixths. 3 of them will fall within the colored 1/2.

Have them refold and fold another time. When they unfold their paper, they will have twelfths. Half of them (6) will fall inside the colored 1/2.

Fold one more time to make 24ths. 12 of them will fall inside the colored 1/2. Here is the progression of fractions for this activity. These are all equivalent fractions.

$$\frac{1}{2} = \frac{3}{6} = \frac{6}{12} = \frac{12}{24}$$

Not only are we learning what equivalent fractions look like, we are noting the pattern and flow of the symbols and how they change each time a new fold is made. What impacts Nom also impacts Num equally!

III. Equivalent fractions and fraction strips

Give your students copies of the colored fraction strips (see Resource 9-1) and have them cut the strips apart.

1. Say, "Find the 1/2 fraction strip. Fold it in half so only 1/2 is showing."

2. "Find as many fractions that you can that are equivalent to 1/2." The students will lay strip after strip by the 1/2 and see which ones are truly equivalent. Ask them to write the fractions side by side on scratch paper. You might need to prompt them as they work: "How many 1/6 sections are the same exact length as the 1/2?" [3]. "Does the 1/5 strip work?" [no].

3. Have them try all the fraction strips against the 1/2 section until they have found all the strips that work.

4. Is there a rule that emerges from this exercise? [Nom has to be an even number in order for fractional parts to be equivalent to 1/2].

5. When you look at the fractions written out side by side, what patterns emerge? Here they are:

$$\frac{1}{2} = \frac{2}{4} = \frac{3}{6} = \frac{4}{8} = \frac{5}{10} = \frac{6}{12}$$

- Num is increasing by 1 each time - notice that it is the same number as the first numerator.
- Nom is increasing by 2 each time - notice that it is the same number as the first denominator.

Repeat the exercise with 2/3 (fold under 1/3 on that strip) and with 3/4 (fold under 1/4).

IV. Move towards using symbols

Let's look at the series of fractions we discussed above. Here they are again:

$$\frac{1}{2} = \frac{2}{4} = \frac{3}{6} = \frac{4}{8} = \frac{5}{10} = \frac{6}{12}$$

Direct the students' attention to the first fraction: 1/2

Ask, "What are we multiplying Num and Nom by to get 2/4? [2. 2x1=2 and 2x2=4 or 2/4].

Ask, "What are we multiplying Num and Nom by to get 3/6? [3. 3x1=3 and 3x2=6 or 3/6].

Ask, "What are we multiplying Num and Nom by to get 4/8? [4. 4x1=4 and 4x2=8 or 4/8].

The next step is to show the students a pair of fractions with a number missing.

What should we do to find the missing number here?

What is 2 multiplied by to get 6? [3. 2 x 3 = 6].

If we multiply 1 by the same thing, we will have our missing number! [1 x 3 = 3].

$$\frac{1}{2} = \frac{\Box}{6}$$

Let's do another problem together. Show the students this problem:

What should we do to find the missing number? How many 2's are in 10? [5. 2 x 5=10]. If we also multiply 1 by 5, we will have our missing number! [1 x 5 = 5].

$$\frac{1}{2} = \frac{\boxed{}}{10}$$

Show the students the following and work them out together:

$$\frac{2}{3} = \frac{\boxed{}}{9} \qquad \frac{3}{4} = \frac{12}{\boxed{}} \qquad \frac{1}{3} = \frac{\boxed{}}{12}$$

In the first example, 2/3 = ?/9, what did we multiply 3 times to get 9? [3]. If we multiply Num or 2 by the same number, we will get our answer. [2x3=6].

In the second example, we multiplied 3 times 4 to get 12, right? So if we multiply 4 times 4 also, we will get 16 for Nom, or 12/16 for an equivalent fraction.

Finally, what did we multiply 3 times to get to 12? [4]. If we multiply 4x1 we will get our answer: 4/12.

Hands On:
Use Resource 9-2 Find the missing numbers in equivalent fractions.

If all goes well, move on to the next resource.

Hands On:
Use Resource 9-3 Find equivalent fractions.

V. Simplifying fractions

Now that we've practiced with creating equivalent fractions for simple fractions, we need to go in the opposite direction and learn to simplify large fractions. Make sure your students have their fraction strips out for this exercise.

First tell this story:

Num and Nom were having a pizza party. What a surprise, right? Well, they had invited 4 friends over. The 6 of them would share a pizza after giving the 2 pets each a slice. Nom cut the pizza into eighths and gave one piece to the dog and one to the cat. Num was all excited because he was going to get to do a lot of counting!

"We had 8 slices of pizza until we gave two to the pets. Now we have 6 slices of pizza left," Num said. "That means we each get to eat one piece!"

Then the phone rang. "Hello, Nom? This is Fitz. I can't come tonight because I have a cough."
Before Nom could even get back into the kitchen to tell Num, the phone rang again. "Hello Nom?
This is Katrina. I can't come tonight because I have the flu." The phone rang again and when Nom
picked it up he heard, "Hello Nom? This is Lewis. I can't come tonight because my bike has flat
tires." Nom went back into the kitchen to break the news to Num that there would only be three of
them to share pizza.

Num and Nom thought about what had happened. First they had a pizza cut into eighths so the
six of them could share a pizza with the pets. The middle picture shows the pizza after they fed the
cat and dog. There were 6/8 left over to split with three people. The last picture shows how much
pizza each of the three friends could eat. Instead of eating 2/8 each, they would eat 1/4 of the pizza.
We can simplify 6/8 to 3/4 because we only need to share the pizza among three people.

  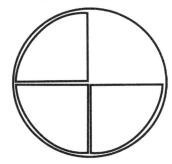

When you go from 6/8 to 3/4, you have done the opposite of what we did before. We would have started with 3/4 and in order to find an equivalent fraction, we would have multiplied both Num and Nom by 2. In this case, to simplify a larger fraction, we are dividing by 2!

Write 6/8 on the whiteboard and ask the students to find another number that they can divide both Num and Nom by. Does 3 work? Nope! You can divide 6 by 3 but not 8. Does 4 work? Nope again! You can divide 8 evenly by 4 but not 6! So 2 it is!

Simplifying fractions using fraction strips:

Write these fractions on a whiteboard:

$$\frac{2}{4} = \frac{3}{6} = \frac{4}{8} = \frac{5}{10}$$

Tell the students that their task is to help you find a fraction with smaller numbers, that you could write for each one.

1. **Start with 2/4.** Is there a fraction that uses smaller numbers that is also equivalent to 2/4? Have the students find their fourths strip and fold it so that 2 fourths are showing. Next, have them find any strips that are equivalent to 2/4. Their goals are to find fractional parts with **smaller numbers but bigger parts** than 2/4. Remember, bigger parts result in smaller numbers. Hopefully the students will figure out that 1/2 is the only fractional part that is equivalent to 2/4 and that also has smaller numbers than 2/4.

Ask the students if they can see what Num and Nom were divided by to arrive at 1/2. The shortcut to reducing 2/4 of course is to divide both numbers by 2, reinforcing the fact that as long as we do the same thing to Nom as we do to Num we're ok! We multiply to get more, smaller fractional parts and we divide to get larger and fewer fractional parts.

2. **Next, work on 3/6.** Ask them to find the fraction strip for sixths and fold the strip so that 3 sixths are showing. This is the fraction we need to reduce. Again, have them explore their fraction strips to find equivalent fractions that have smaller numbers. If needed, ask them if fifths would work. [No. Neither 2/5 nor 3/5 is equivalent to 3/6]. How about fourths? [Yes! 2/4 are equivalent to 3/6. But 2/4 is not simplified as much as it can be as the goal is to use the smallest numbers possible]. How about thirds? [Nope, thirds don't work]. Finally, try halves. This works! When you compare 3/6 to 1/2, what did we need to do to 3/6 to turn it into 1/2? [Divide each number by 3].

3. **Repeat the process with 4/8.** The students will find that sevenths, sixths, fifths won't work. Again 2/4 will work. Does this begin to ring a bell? [It is the same fraction we have seen twice already]. What can we reduce 2/4 down to? [1/2 again].

4. **End with 5/10.** This time ask the students what they think might happen before they even start to work. If they guess that they will end up with 1/2, ask them why they think that might be the case. Direct their attention to the four fractions and ask what pattern they see. [Num is half as large as Nom in every fraction and every fraction can be simplified down to 1/2]. The "rule" we can take away from this is that if the top number is exactly half as large as the bottom number, the simplest form of the fraction is 1/2.

VI. Patterns that emerge when simplifying fractions

Let's look at some really large fractions and practice reducing to their simplest form. Write these fractions on the whiteboard:

$$\frac{200}{400} \quad \frac{150}{300} \quad \frac{420}{840} \quad \frac{125}{250}$$

In each case, the top number is half the size of the bottom number.

You can verify this by asking, "How many 200s are in 200? [1]. How many 200s are in 400? [2 so we can reduce 200/400 to its simplest form of 1/2].

Ask, "How many 150s are in 150? [1]. How many 150s are in 300? [2, so the simplest fraction is 1/2]

Ask, "How many 420s are in 420? [1]. How many 420s are in 840? [2, so the simplest fraction is 1/2].

Ask, "How many 125s are in 125? [1]. How many 125s are in 250? [2, so the simplest fraction is 1/2].

$$\frac{1^{\times 200}}{2_{\times 200}} = \frac{200^{\div 200}}{400_{\div 200}} = \frac{1}{2}$$

This illustration shows the complete process. You can start with 1/2, multiply Num and Nom by 200 and reach 200/400. Then to reduce back down, you just divide both Num and Nom by the same number: 200.

1. Some fractions automatically will equal 1/2 if the Numerator is exactly half of the Denominator:

$$\frac{200}{400} \quad \frac{150}{300} \quad \frac{420}{840} \quad \frac{125}{250}$$

2. If both numbers are even numbers, divide by 2 as many times as you can:

$$\frac{32}{256}^{\div 2} \quad \frac{16}{128}^{\div 2} \quad \frac{8}{64}^{\div 2} \quad \frac{4}{32}^{\div 2} \quad \frac{2}{16}^{\div 2} \quad \frac{1}{8}$$

3. When both Num and Nom end in zero, you can simplify by crossing off zeros:

$$\frac{2400}{10,800} \quad \frac{24}{108}^{\div 2} \quad \frac{12}{54}^{\div 2} \quad \frac{6}{27}^{\div 3} \quad \frac{2}{9}$$

4. If you cannot divide both numbers by 2, try three's:

$$\frac{243}{324}^{\div 3} \quad \frac{81}{108}^{\div 3} \quad \frac{27}{36}^{\div 3} \quad \frac{9}{12}^{\div 3} \quad \frac{3}{4}$$

5. For fractions ending in 0 and 5, try dividing by 5:

$$\frac{250}{375}^{\div 5} \quad \frac{50}{75}^{\div 5} \quad \frac{10}{15}^{\div 5} \quad \frac{2}{3}$$

Hands On:

Give the students Resource 9-4 and offer support as needed.

When you feel your students are ready for it, give them the assessment using Resource 9-5.

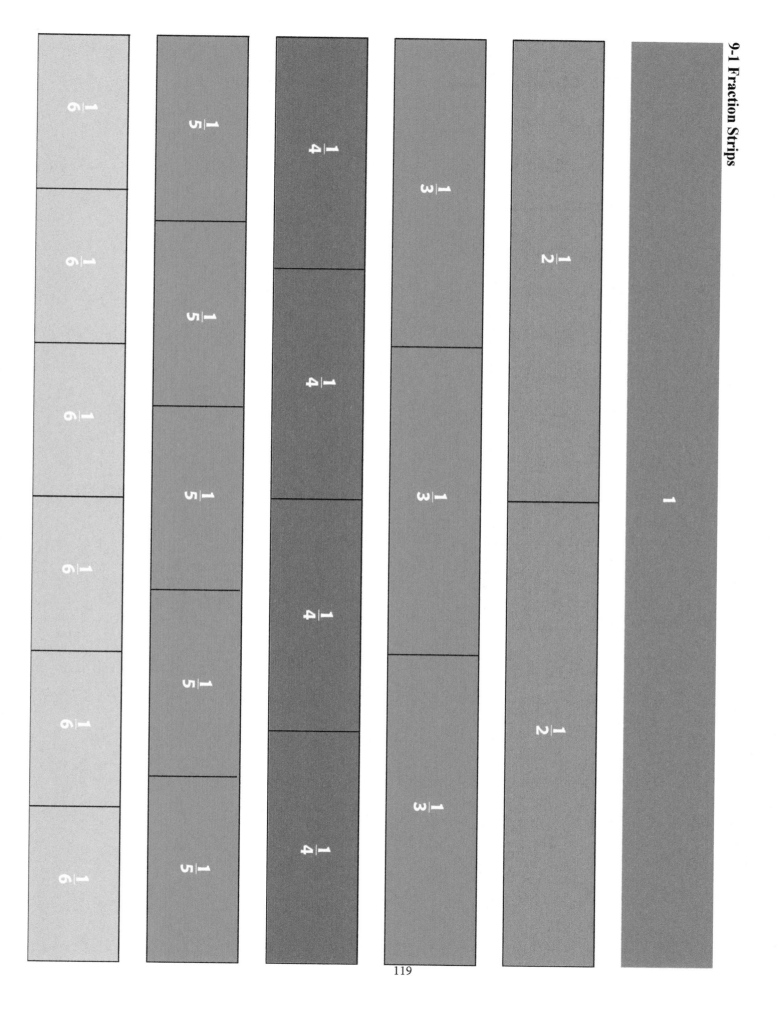

$\frac{1}{12}$	$\frac{1}{11}$	$\frac{1}{10}$	$\frac{1}{9}$	$\frac{1}{8}$	$\frac{1}{7}$
$\frac{1}{12}$	$\frac{1}{11}$	$\frac{1}{10}$	$\frac{1}{9}$	$\frac{1}{8}$	$\frac{1}{7}$
$\frac{1}{12}$	$\frac{1}{11}$	$\frac{1}{10}$	$\frac{1}{9}$	$\frac{1}{8}$	$\frac{1}{7}$
$\frac{1}{12}$	$\frac{1}{11}$	$\frac{1}{10}$	$\frac{1}{9}$	$\frac{1}{8}$	$\frac{1}{7}$
$\frac{1}{12}$	$\frac{1}{11}$	$\frac{1}{10}$	$\frac{1}{9}$	$\frac{1}{8}$	$\frac{1}{7}$
$\frac{1}{12}$	$\frac{1}{11}$	$\frac{1}{10}$	$\frac{1}{9}$	$\frac{1}{8}$	$\frac{1}{7}$
$\frac{1}{12}$	$\frac{1}{11}$	$\frac{1}{10}$	$\frac{1}{9}$	$\frac{1}{8}$	$\frac{1}{7}$
$\frac{1}{12}$	$\frac{1}{11}$	$\frac{1}{10}$	$\frac{1}{9}$	$\frac{1}{8}$	
$\frac{1}{12}$	$\frac{1}{11}$	$\frac{1}{10}$	$\frac{1}{9}$		
$\frac{1}{12}$	$\frac{1}{11}$	$\frac{1}{10}$	$\frac{1}{9}$		
$\frac{1}{12}$	$\frac{1}{11}$				
$\frac{1}{12}$	$\frac{1}{11}$				

9-2 Find the missing numbers

For each problem below, figure out the missing number. The first one is done for you.

1. $\dfrac{1}{2} \overset{x2}{\underset{x2}{=}} \dfrac{2}{4}$

2. $\dfrac{1}{2} = \dfrac{}{6}$

3. $\dfrac{1}{2} = \dfrac{}{10}$

4. $\dfrac{2}{3} = \dfrac{}{6}$

5. $\dfrac{2}{3} = \dfrac{}{9}$

6. $\dfrac{2}{3} = \dfrac{}{12}$

7. $\dfrac{3}{4} = \dfrac{}{8}$

8. $\dfrac{3}{4} = \dfrac{}{12}$

9. $\dfrac{3}{4} = \dfrac{}{16}$

10. $\dfrac{1}{2} = \dfrac{3}{}$

11. $\dfrac{1}{2} = \dfrac{4}{}$

12. $\dfrac{2}{3} = \dfrac{6}{}$

13. $\dfrac{2}{3} = \dfrac{8}{}$

14. $\dfrac{3}{4} = \dfrac{9}{}$

15. $\dfrac{3}{4} = \dfrac{12}{}$

16. $\dfrac{3}{4} = \dfrac{6}{}$

9-3 Find equivalent fractions

Name_____

For each fraction given below, supply two equivalent fractions. The first one is done for you.

1. $\dfrac{1}{2}\,\overset{+1}{\underset{+2}{=}}\,\dfrac{2}{4}\,\overset{+1}{\underset{+2}{=}}\,\dfrac{3}{6}$

2. $\dfrac{1}{3} = \rule{1cm}{0.4pt} = \rule{1cm}{0.4pt}$

3. $\dfrac{1}{4} = \rule{1cm}{0.4pt} = \rule{1cm}{0.4pt}$

4. $\dfrac{2}{3} = \rule{1cm}{0.4pt} = \rule{1cm}{0.4pt}$

5. $\dfrac{2}{5} = \rule{1cm}{0.4pt} = \rule{1cm}{0.4pt}$

6. $\dfrac{4}{5} = \rule{1cm}{0.4pt} = \rule{1cm}{0.4pt}$

7. $\dfrac{7}{8} = \rule{1cm}{0.4pt} = \rule{1cm}{0.4pt}$

8. $\dfrac{5}{6} = \rule{1cm}{0.4pt} = \rule{1cm}{0.4pt}$

9. $\dfrac{3}{4} = \rule{1cm}{0.4pt} = \rule{1cm}{0.4pt}$

10. $\dfrac{3}{2} = \rule{1cm}{0.4pt} = \rule{1cm}{0.4pt}$

11. $\dfrac{4}{3} = \rule{1cm}{0.4pt} = \rule{1cm}{0.4pt}$

12. $\dfrac{3}{5} = \rule{1cm}{0.4pt} = \rule{1cm}{0.4pt}$

13. $\dfrac{3}{6} = \rule{1cm}{0.4pt} = \rule{1cm}{0.4pt}$

14. $\dfrac{7}{9} = \rule{1cm}{0.4pt} = \rule{1cm}{0.4pt}$

15. $\dfrac{9}{10} = \rule{1cm}{0.4pt} = \rule{1cm}{0.4pt}$

16. $\dfrac{2}{4} = \rule{1cm}{0.4pt} = \rule{1cm}{0.4pt}$

9-4 Simplifying fractions

Simplify each fraction below by treating Num and Nom exactly the same. What you do to one, do to the other!

1. $\dfrac{16}{24}\substack{\div 2 \\ \div 2} = \dfrac{8}{12}\substack{\div 2 \\ \div 2} = \dfrac{4}{6}\substack{\div 2 \\ \div 2} = \dfrac{2}{3}$

2. $\dfrac{12}{16} =$

3. $\dfrac{21}{24} =$

4. $\dfrac{30}{45} =$

5. $\dfrac{18}{24} =$

6. $\dfrac{4}{8} =$

7. $\dfrac{14}{18} =$

8. $\dfrac{100}{600} =$

9-5 What I know about equivalent fractions   Name_____

Fill in the missing numbers to make equivalent fractions for each original fraction.

1. $\dfrac{1}{2} = \dfrac{}{6}$

2. $\dfrac{1}{2} = \dfrac{}{10}$

3. $\dfrac{2}{3} = \dfrac{}{15}$

4. $\dfrac{3}{4} = \dfrac{}{12}$

5. $\dfrac{3}{5} = \dfrac{}{20}$

6. $\dfrac{1}{2} = \dfrac{}{12}$

7. $\dfrac{1}{2} = \dfrac{}{8}$

8. $\dfrac{2}{5} = \dfrac{}{15}$

9. $\dfrac{1}{4} = \dfrac{}{16}$

10. $\dfrac{3}{4} = \dfrac{}{20}$

In this section, simplify the fractions the quickest way possible.

11. $\dfrac{200}{500} =$

12. $\dfrac{150}{300} =$

13. $\dfrac{400}{700} =$

9-5 What I know about equivalent fractions

Name_____

In this section, simplify the fractions. Use the space to the right for figuring.

14. $\dfrac{16}{24} =$

15. $\dfrac{12}{16} =$

16. $\dfrac{30}{45} =$

17. $\dfrac{15}{21} =$

18. $\dfrac{12}{18} =$

ADDING FRACTIONS

Goals for This Chapter:

1. Adding fractions with like denominators
2. Learn what Least Common Denominator means
3. Learn how to find the Least Common Denominator
4. Adding fractions, changing one denominator
5. Adding fractions, changing both denominators

I. Number Sense for Adding Fractions

Rather than just memorizing rules, we are going to do a lot of hands-on work so students will understand what is going on when we add fractions. If they work concepts out first, the "rules" will emerge and will be far easier to remember.

Preparation:

Distribute copies of Resource 10-1 and ask the students to very carefully cut out the shapes right on the lines provided. The students will also need their fraction strips (Resource 9-1).

Pattern Discovery

Before actually beginning to add fractions, let's explore using fraction strips. Use Resource 10-2 so the students can record their discoveries.

1. Have the students place the 1/2 strip in front of them on the desk. Now, have them choose the 1/3 strip and line it up with the 1/2.

2. **Ask** the students to check to see if the center line of the 1/2 strip lines up with any dividing lines on the 1/3 strip. [No].

3. **Ask** them to take the 1/4 strip and line it up with 1/2. Do the center dividing lines match? [Yes].

4. They will write 1/4 beside 1/2 and record how many fractional parts fit into each half [2].

This illustration shows that 1/2 and 1/3 strips do NOT line up, but 1/2 and 1/4 DO line up.

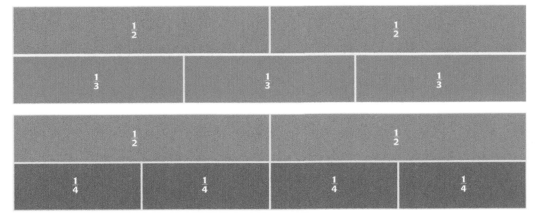

5. Students will continue checking fraction strips against their 1/2 strip. The ones that line up they will record on their chart, also noting how many of the fractional parts fit into each half.

[The fraction strips that work with 1/2 are 1/4, 1/6, 1/8, 1/10, and 1/12.]

Ask: Why do these particular fraction strips line up with 1/2 when the others don't? [The denominators are all even and can be divided by 2. The odd denominators cannot be divided by 2].

Repeat the activity, but this time the strips are going to be compared to the 1/3 strip.

1. Start by laying the 1/4 strip by the 1/3 strip and seeing if they line up. If they don't line up, set the 1/4 strip aside and try 1/5.

2. **Ask,** "Do you think all the odd denominators will line up correctly with the 1/3 fraction strip?" Don't tell them the answer, just hear their best guesses and challenge them to try all their fraction strips and find out which line up and which don't.

3. For each strip, record as before if they line up and if so, how many fractional parts fit into each third. [The fraction strips that line up with 1/3 are 1/6, 1/9, 1/12.]

Ask: "What do these denominators have in common?" [They can all be divided by 3].

Repeat the activity, but this time the strips are going to be compared to the 1/4 strip.

The fractions that line up with 1/4 are 1/8 and 1/12. Each of the denominators can be divided by 4.

Repeat the activity with the 1/5 strip.

The only fraction that lines up with 1/5 is 1/10. **Ask** the students to guess what other fractions might work if they had strips for them. [1/15 and 1/20 - both can be divided by 5].

Table of Equivalent Fractions

$\frac{1}{2}$	$\frac{2}{4}$	$\frac{3}{6}$	$\frac{4}{8}$	$\frac{5}{10}$	$\frac{6}{12}$	$\frac{7}{14}$	$\frac{8}{16}$	$\frac{9}{18}$	$\frac{10}{20}$
$\frac{1}{3}$	$\frac{2}{6}$	$\frac{3}{9}$	$\frac{4}{12}$	$\frac{5}{15}$	$\frac{6}{18}$	$\frac{7}{21}$			
$\frac{1}{4}$	$\frac{2}{8}$	$\frac{3}{12}$	$\frac{4}{16}$	$\frac{5}{20}$	$\frac{6}{24}$				
$\frac{1}{5}$	$\frac{2}{10}$	$\frac{3}{15}$	$\frac{4}{20}$	$\frac{5}{25}$					
$\frac{1}{6}$	$\frac{2}{12}$	$\frac{3}{18}$	$\frac{4}{24}$						
$\frac{1}{7}$	$\frac{2}{14}$	$\frac{3}{21}$							
$\frac{1}{8}$	$\frac{2}{16}$	$\frac{3}{24}$							
$\frac{1}{9}$	$\frac{2}{18}$	$\frac{3}{27}$							
$\frac{1}{10}$	$\frac{2}{20}$	$\frac{3}{30}$							
$\frac{1}{11}$	$\frac{2}{22}$	$\frac{3}{33}$							
$\frac{1}{12}$	$\frac{2}{24}$	$\frac{3}{36}$							

Now ask the students if there were some fraction strips that didn't line up with any of the strips so far. [1/7 and 1/11].

Ask: "Why do you think these two fraction strips are left out? Is it because they are odd?" [No, because 1/3, 1/5 and 1/9 are also odd].

Ask: "Can 7 or 11 be divided by any number except 1?" [No.]

The illustration on the left shows the information we distilled so far. In each row, the denominator increases by the number in the first denominator, while the numerators increase by 1.

II. Adding fractions with like denominators

Adding fractions with like denominators will be so easy for your students given the background knowledge they have! In Chapter 4, Num learned from Nom that in order for him to count things, they had to be the same. He could count trees, or clouds, or rocks or fourths or tenths, but he couldn't mix them up. Same rule applies for adding fractional parts. The denominators have to be the same in order to do simple addition. Let your students figure out the rule from doing the exercises with models. For this section, have the students use their clock face models. If they stack up the parts by fractional part, it will help this process go much better! (If you have students who struggle when handling many little pieces, let them use the fraction strips for this exercise.)

We will start with adding fractional parts that equal 1 whole or less.

Tell the students that you will write a problem on the whiteboard and they will use their fraction models to solve.

1. Add 3/5 + 2/5	[5/5 or 1]	6. Add 1/3 + 1/3	[2/3]
2. Add 2/9 + 4/9	[6/9 or 1/3]	7. Add 3/8 + 4/8	[7/8]
3. Add 3/7 + 1/7	[4/7]	8. Add 1/4 + 2/4	[3/4]
4. Add 3/10 + 5/10	[8/10 or 4/5]	9. Add 2/6 + 3/6	[5/6]
5. Add 5/12 + 6/12	[11/12]		

When the students start just looking at the problem you wrote and calling out the answer without needing models, you can be pretty sure they have gotten the content of this section! **Ask:** "What have you learned about adding fractions when Nom is the same?" [If the Noms are the same, you can just add the Nums].

Hands On:
Use Resource 10-4 Adding fractions with like denominators to give students practice with pencil and paper.

Next, we will add fractional parts that equal more than 1 whole.

The students will use Resource 10-5 in this section. Do the first few problems with them as needed. They will be adding the fractions and of course will have an improper fraction which they should simplify. If you feel students will become bogged down in the process, I would recommend having them add all the problems first and then go back and simplify. The concept they will need to reinforce in this section is that you make a whole from a fraction with the same Num as Nom: 3/3 or 4/4 or 5/5, etc. So 7/10 + 5/10 = 12/10. If you take 10/10 away to make a whole, you have 2/10 left over. The answer, simplified, is 1 2/10.

III. Adding fractions - changing 1 denominator

In this section, we will be adding fractions when one denominator is exactly twice as large as the other. For instance, we will be adding 2/3 + 1/6. The second denominator is double that of the first, so students will be changing only one denominator so that it matches the other one. In this case, they will change 1/3 to 2/6 so that both denominators are the same. It is simple to see what the smaller denominator needs to change to if we use fraction strips. Here we can see that 1/3 is equal to 2/6 and that 2/3=4/6, and that 4/6+1/6=5/6.

	$\frac{1}{3}$	
$\frac{1}{6}$	$\frac{1}{6}$	$\frac{1}{6}$	$\frac{1}{6}$	$\frac{1}{6}$	$\frac{1}{6}$

Let's introduce this concept with a story.

Num and Nom were hungry. They pulled their left over pizza out of the fridge. This is what they saw: One pan had two large slices in it and the second pan had two smaller slices in it. They wanted to share all the pizza equally between them. Nom took a pizza cutter and cut the large pieces in half so they would match the smaller pieces.

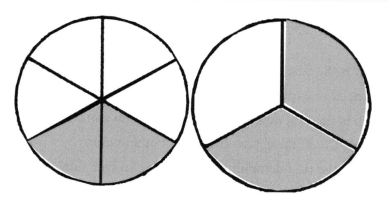

Students will be using what they learned in Chapter 9 regarding equivalent fractions. Let them use their models as needed to solve these problems, challenging them to move towards solving in their heads.

Do a few problems together using Resource 10-6. In each of these problems, the students will be cutting the larger pizza slices in half in order to solve the problems. They will need to rewrite the fractions they "cut" in half before adding.

1. Add 1/3+1/6   [3/6]
2. Add 3/4+1/8   [7/8]
3. Add 1/4+1/2   [3/4]

4. Add 1/6+1/12   [3/12]
5. Add 2/5+3/10   [7/10]

Hands On:
Use Resource 10-7 Adding fractions; change one denominator to give students practice with pencil and paper.

IV. Adding fractions - changing 2 denominators

Now the real fun starts! In this section, we will be working on adding fractions where both denominators have to change. Have your students take out the Table of Equivalent Fractions so we can explore some patterns before we start. (Resource 10-3).

Here is a smaller version of the Table.

Table of Equivalent Fractions

$\frac{1}{2}$	$\frac{2}{4}$	$\frac{3}{6}$	$\frac{4}{8}$	$\frac{5}{10}$	$\frac{6}{12}$	$\frac{7}{14}$	$\frac{8}{16}$	$\frac{9}{18}$	$\frac{10}{20}$
$\frac{1}{3}$	$\frac{2}{6}$	$\frac{3}{9}$	$\frac{4}{12}$	$\frac{5}{15}$	$\frac{6}{18}$	$\frac{7}{21}$			
$\frac{1}{4}$	$\frac{2}{8}$	$\frac{3}{12}$	$\frac{4}{16}$	$\frac{5}{20}$	$\frac{6}{24}$				
$\frac{1}{5}$	$\frac{2}{10}$	$\frac{3}{15}$	$\frac{4}{20}$	$\frac{5}{25}$					
$\frac{1}{6}$	$\frac{2}{12}$	$\frac{3}{18}$	$\frac{4}{24}$						
$\frac{1}{7}$	$\frac{2}{14}$	$\frac{3}{21}$							
$\frac{1}{8}$	$\frac{2}{16}$	$\frac{3}{24}$							
$\frac{1}{9}$	$\frac{2}{18}$	$\frac{3}{27}$							
$\frac{1}{10}$	$\frac{2}{20}$	$\frac{3}{30}$							
$\frac{1}{11}$	$\frac{2}{22}$	$\frac{3}{33}$							
$\frac{1}{12}$	$\frac{2}{24}$	$\frac{3}{36}$							

1. Discuss with the students the patterns that exist in this Table. Starting with the 1/2 row, note that the denominators are also multiples of 2. You can count by 2s. In the 1/3 row, the denominators are all multiples of 3; you can count by 3s. In the 1/4 row, the denominators are multiples of 4; you can count up by 4s. And the pattern continues with all the other fractions.

2. Next, begin to compare denominators from the 1/2 and 1/3 rows. **Ask:** "Which is the smallest denominator they both have in common?" [6]. This is because both 2 and 3 go into 6. The REALLY cool thing to notice is that there are three 2s in 6 and two 3s in 6. Have the children circle those two denominators.

3. Now compare the 1/2 and 1/4 rows. **Ask:** "Which is the first denominator they both have in common?" [4. This is because 2 goes equally into 4. So we don't need to explore further!]

4. Now compare the 1/2 and 1/5 rows. **Ask:** "Which is the first denominator they both have in common?" [10]. Notice that there are five 2s in 10 and two 5s in 10! Circle these two 10s with another color.

5. Check out the rows for 1/2 and 1/6. **Ask:** "Which is the first denominator they have in common?" [6 - so we don't need to explore further. What this means is that 2 divides evenly into 6].

6. Now look at the rows for 1/2 and 1/7. **Ask:** "Which denominator do they both have in common?" [14]. Notice also that the same amazing pattern continues here. There are two 7s in 14 and seven 2s in 14!

7. Finish comparing the rows with the 1/2 row, making sure the patterns continue as they have begun.

The next step in pattern discovery is to have the children compare other pairs of rows.

1. Have the students compare 1/3 and 1/4 rows. Find the first number they both go into evenly. [12]

2. Compare rows 1/3 and 1/5 to find the first number they both go into evenly. [15].

3. Because 3 goes into 6 evenly, we can skip comparing 1/3 and 1/6. Compare 1/3 and 1/7 instead.

Continue on like this until the students are familiar with how to find what they will learn to call the Lowest Common Denominator.

Introduce the term "Lowest Common Denominator"

See the illustration below. This shows a student finding a lowest common denominator. We use a ladder, so the students can relate the **lowest** number to the **lower** rungs on the ladder. As the student looks up the ladder rungs, he is crossing off the numbers that are not **common** to both ladders. He put a star behind the 12s because they are the two numbers 3 and 4 have in **common**!

If you feel your students would benefit from making ladders such as these with the multiples of each number on them, please use Resource 10-8. They will need one for each number from 2 to 12. This way, when they want to use a tactile method to locate a lowest common denominator, they can just grab the two ladders that represent the denominators they are working with. Use Resource 10-9 to give your students practice with finding LCD mentally. You can give them this same sheet multiple times and see if their fluency improves. The more automatic this process becomes, the easier computing with fractions will be.

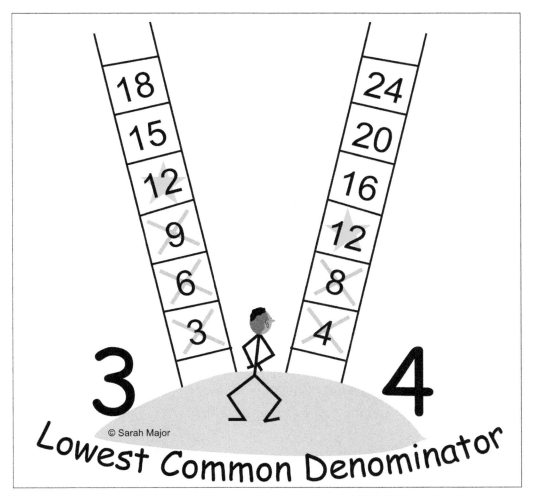

What the term means: LOWEST on the ladder, the one number in COMMON, and it will be used as the DENOMINATOR for both fractions.

Let's do some addition now!

At this point, your students have made ladders, or will be using the Table of Equivalent Fractions, or they might be at the point where they can find LCD (lowest common denominators) in their heads. It is time to work some addition together. We will start with problems where the numerators are all 1s.

1. Add 1/3+1/5   LCD is 15.   1/3=5/15 while 1/5=3/15.   Therefore, 5/15+3/15=8/15.

2. Add 1/2+1/5   LCD is 10.   1/2=5/10 while 1/5=2/10.   Therefore, 5/10+2/10=7/10.

3. Add 1/4+1/5   LCD is 20.   1/4=5/20 while 1/5=4/20.   Therefore, 5/20+4/20=9/20.

4. Add 1/2+1/3   LCD is 6.   1/2=3/6 while 1/3=2/6.   Therefore, 3/6+2/6=5/6.

Add 1/3 + 1/5

1. Ask the students to grab their ladders for 3s and 5s. Starting at the bottom, ask them to find the first number both ladders have in common. This number [15] will be the new denominator as they rewrite each of the fractions. They will need their 15th clock face and their 1/3 and 1/5 pieces.

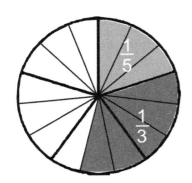

2. Students will lay 1/5 and 1/3 fraction pieces on the 1/15 clockface with edges touching. They will see that 1/5 becomes 3/15 and 1/3 becomes 5/15. This will show them clearly how to rewrite the two fractions so they are both using 15 as LCD. You might want to point out that when we look at the 5s ladder, you climb 3 steps up to reach 15. Three is also the number of 15ths inside the 1/5 piece. Look at the 3s ladder and note that in order to reach 15, you climb up 5 rungs. Five is also the number of 15ths inside the 1/3 piece.

3. Finally, they will add 5/15 and 3/15. The answer is 8/15.

Add 1/2 + 1/5

1. Grab ladders for 2 and 5 and climb the rungs to find the LCD. [10 - Five steps for the 2s ladder and two steps for the 5s ladder]. Students will need their 10ths clock face and the 1/2 and 1/5 fraction pieces.

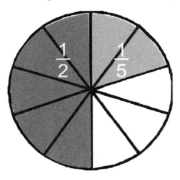

2. Students will lay 1/5 and 1/2 fraction pieces on the 1/10 clockface with edges touching. They will see that 1/5 becomes 2/10 and 1/2 becomes 5/10. This will show them clearly how to rewrite the two fractions so they are both using 10 as LCD. Point out that on the 5s ladder, you climb 2 steps up to reach 10. Two is also the number of 10ths inside the 1/5 piece. On the 3s ladder, note that in order to reach 10, you climb up 5 rungs. Five is also the number of 10ths inside the 1/2 piece.

3. Add the new fractions. [7/10].

Add 1/4 + 1/5

1. Find the ladders for 4s and 5s. Climb the rungs to find the LCD [20 - five steps for 4s and four steps for 5s]. Students will need the clock face for 20ths and the 1/4 and 1/5 pieces.

2. Students will lay 1/4 and 1/5 fraction pieces on the 1/20 clockface with edges touching. They will see that 1/5 becomes 4/20 and 1/4 becomes 5/20. Tie the rewriting of the fractions to the ladders as we did before.

3. Add the new fractions. [9/20].

Add 1/2 + 1/3

1. Find ladders for 2s and 3s and begin to climb. 6 is the LCD. You climbed 3 rungs on the 2s ladder and two rungs on the 3s ladder. Use clock face for 1/6 and the pieces for 1/2 and 1/3.

2. Rewrite the fractions. Both denominators are 6. Multiply each numerator by the correct number.

3. Add the new fractions. [5/6].

Hands On:

Use Resource 10-10 to give students practice with finding LCD. The more fluent they are with finding LCD, the more quickly they will be able to solve addition problems.

Practice for fluency:

Use Resource 10-11 and 10-12 to provide pencil and paper practice with fractions. Take the time to find out the students' best ways of finding LCD - it might be that some students prefer using fraction strips, for some it might be that using the clock faces seems more natural, and others might prefer to work out the problems using multiplication and division to find the LCD. Encourage each student to think about what they prefer and use that method. It is more important for children to learn how they learn best than it is for them to try and just memorize procedures we give them, and in particular, memorization is not a visual learner's best tool.

On the next page, you will see an illustration of how to use ladders to find LCD, rewriting the fractions, and finally adding them. I would not display this image until after students have used real models such as clock faces and fractional parts to solve addition problems when denominators are different.

Hands On:

When you feel the students are ready, give them the assessment (Resource 10-13).

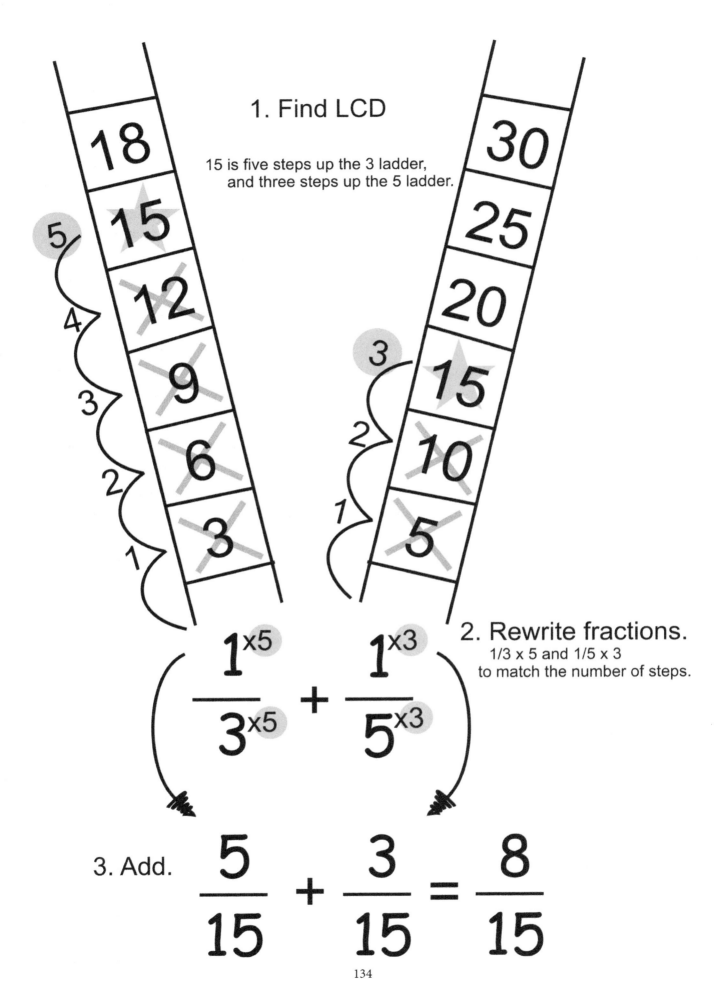

1. Find LCD

15 is five steps up the 3 ladder,
and three steps up the 5 ladder.

18		30
15		25
12		20
9		15
6		10
3		5

2. Rewrite fractions.
1/3 x 5 and 1/5 x 3
to match the number of steps.

$$\frac{1^{\times 5}}{3^{\times 5}} + \frac{1^{\times 3}}{5^{\times 3}}$$

3. Add. $\dfrac{5}{15} + \dfrac{3}{15} = \dfrac{8}{15}$

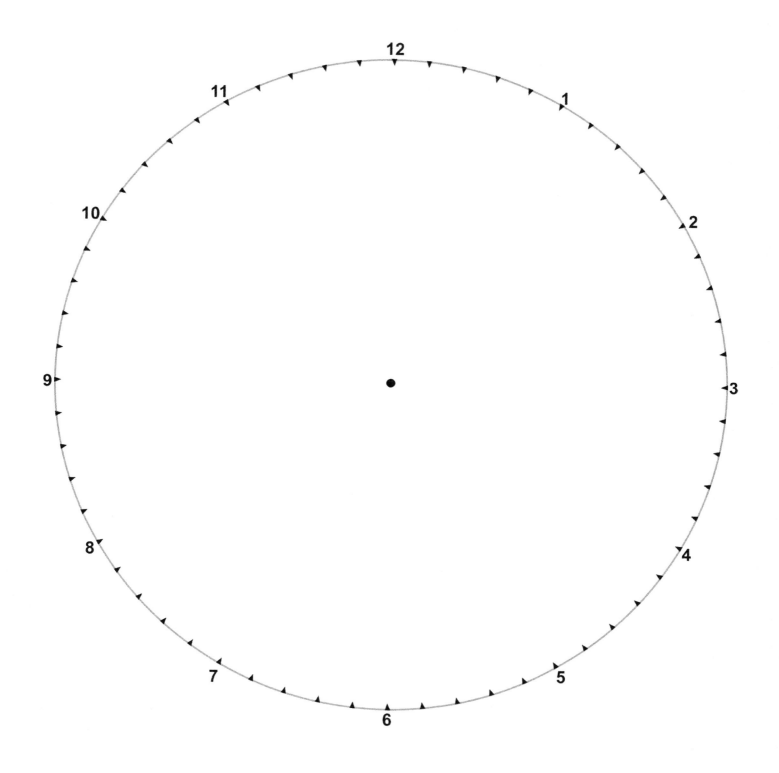

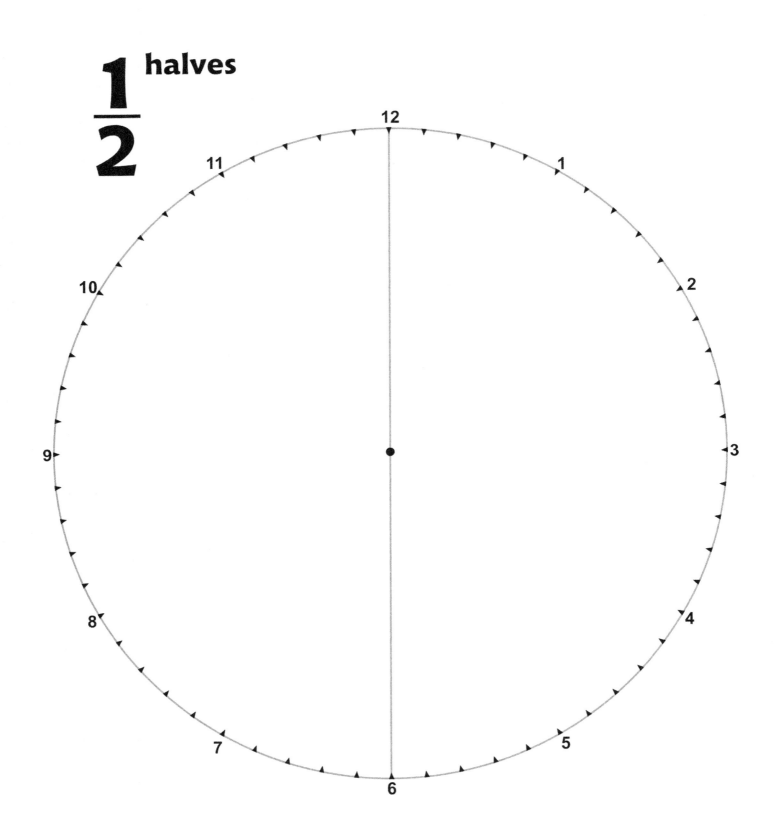

$$\frac{1}{2}\text{ halves}$$

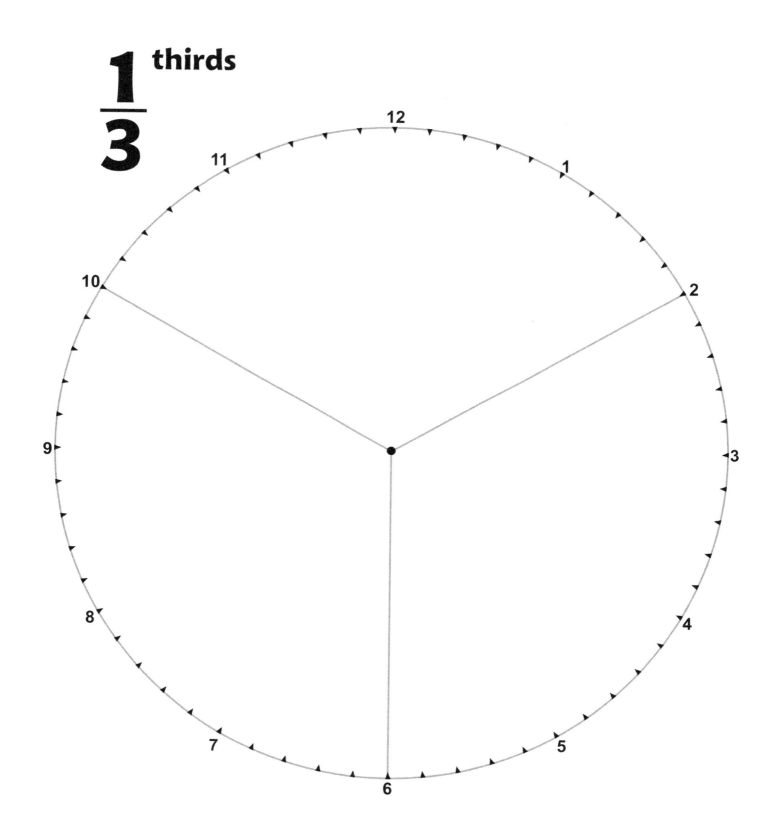

1 fourths
4

Name_____

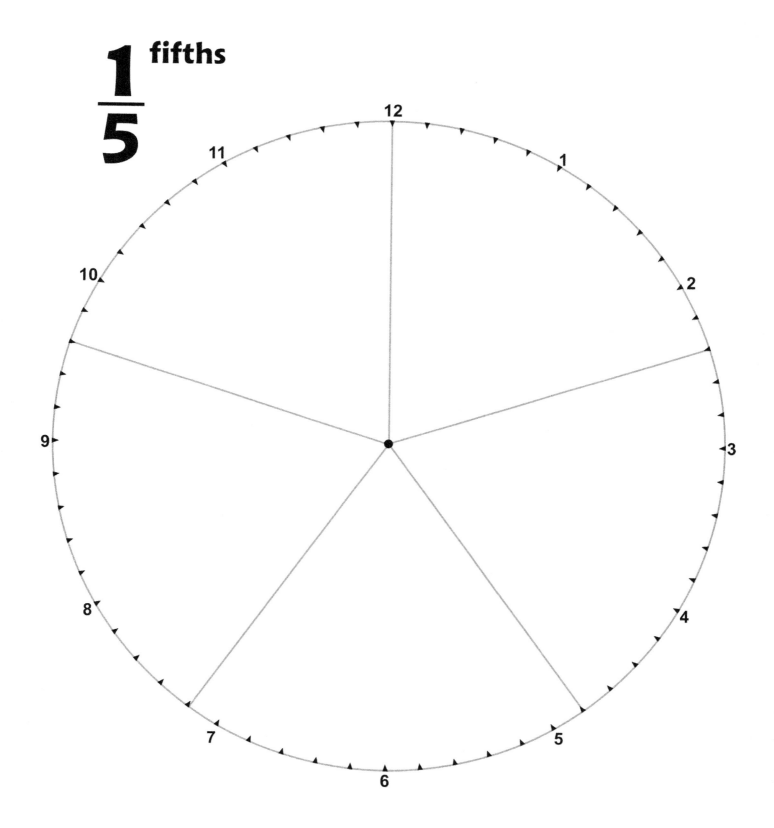

$\dfrac{1}{6}$ **sixths**

$\dfrac{1}{8}$ **eighths**

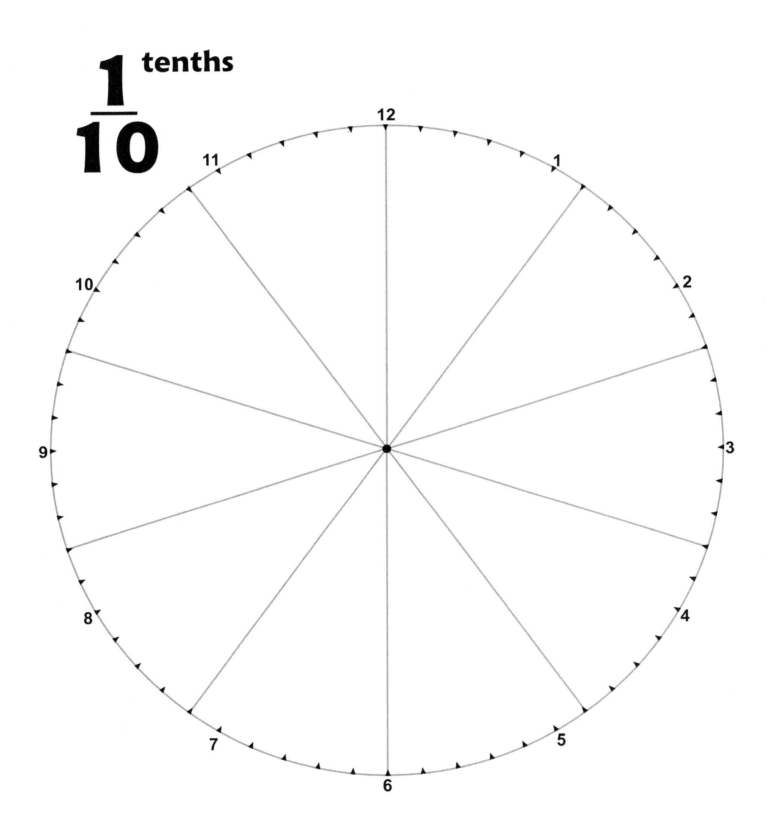

1/12 twelfths

10-2 Table of equivalent fractions

Name_____

Use this chart to record the fraction strips that line up with each of the fractions in the first column. When you have finished recording the fractions on your fraction strips, see if you can continue the pattern and create more fractions that would fit.

$\frac{1}{2}$	——	——	——	——	——	——	——	——	——
$\frac{1}{3}$	——	——	——	——	——	——			
$\frac{1}{4}$	——	——	——	——	——				
$\frac{1}{5}$	——	——	——	——					
$\frac{1}{6}$	——	——	——						
$\frac{1}{7}$	——	——							
$\frac{1}{8}$	——	——							
$\frac{1}{9}$	——	——							
$\frac{1}{10}$	——	——							
$\frac{1}{11}$	——	——							
$\frac{1}{12}$	——	——							

Name_____

Table of Equivalent Fractions

$\frac{1}{2}$	$\frac{2}{4}$	$\frac{3}{6}$	$\frac{4}{8}$	$\frac{5}{10}$	$\frac{6}{12}$	$\frac{7}{14}$	$\frac{8}{16}$	$\frac{9}{18}$	$\frac{10}{20}$
$\frac{1}{3}$	$\frac{2}{6}$	$\frac{3}{9}$	$\frac{4}{12}$	$\frac{5}{15}$	$\frac{6}{18}$	$\frac{7}{21}$			
$\frac{1}{4}$	$\frac{2}{8}$	$\frac{3}{12}$	$\frac{4}{16}$	$\frac{5}{20}$	$\frac{6}{24}$				
$\frac{1}{5}$	$\frac{2}{10}$	$\frac{3}{15}$	$\frac{4}{20}$	$\frac{5}{25}$					
$\frac{1}{6}$	$\frac{2}{12}$	$\frac{3}{18}$	$\frac{4}{24}$						
$\frac{1}{7}$	$\frac{2}{14}$	$\frac{3}{21}$							
$\frac{1}{8}$	$\frac{2}{16}$	$\frac{3}{24}$							
$\frac{1}{9}$	$\frac{2}{18}$	$\frac{3}{27}$							
$\frac{1}{10}$	$\frac{2}{20}$	$\frac{3}{30}$							
$\frac{1}{11}$	$\frac{2}{22}$	$\frac{3}{33}$							
$\frac{1}{12}$	$\frac{2}{24}$	$\frac{3}{36}$							

10-4 Adding fractions with like denominators

Name_____

Add the fractions and write the answers. Remember, when deNOMinators are the same, all you have to do is add NUMerators.

1. $\dfrac{1}{4} + \dfrac{2}{4} =$

2. $\dfrac{1}{3} + \dfrac{1}{3} =$

3. $\dfrac{3}{8} + \dfrac{4}{8} =$

4. $\dfrac{1}{5} + \dfrac{2}{5} =$

5. $\dfrac{1}{6} + \dfrac{4}{6} =$

6. $\dfrac{2}{7} + \dfrac{3}{7} =$

7. $\dfrac{3}{8} + \dfrac{1}{8} =$

8. $\dfrac{3}{9} + \dfrac{2}{9} =$

9. $\dfrac{3}{6} + \dfrac{2}{6} =$

10. $\dfrac{2}{4} + \dfrac{2}{4} =$

11. $\dfrac{4}{9} + \dfrac{2}{9} =$

12. $\dfrac{1}{3} + \dfrac{2}{3} =$

13. $\dfrac{2}{8} + \dfrac{5}{8} =$

14. $\dfrac{4}{7} + \dfrac{2}{7} =$

15. $\dfrac{4}{10} + \dfrac{5}{10} =$

16. $\dfrac{3}{5} + \dfrac{1}{5} =$

10-5 Adding fractions that will equal more than a whole   Name_____

Add these fractions. They will be improper fractions, so after you have added all the fractions, go back and simplify each one.

1. $\dfrac{3}{4} + \dfrac{2}{4} =$

2. $\dfrac{2}{3} + \dfrac{2}{3} =$

3. $\dfrac{7}{8} + \dfrac{4}{8} =$

4. $\dfrac{4}{5} + \dfrac{3}{5} =$

5. $\dfrac{3}{6} + \dfrac{4}{6} =$

6. $\dfrac{5}{7} + \dfrac{4}{7} =$

7. $\dfrac{5}{8} + \dfrac{5}{8} =$

8. $\dfrac{7}{9} + \dfrac{5}{9} =$

9. $\dfrac{1}{3} + \dfrac{4}{3} =$

10. $\dfrac{3}{4} + \dfrac{3}{4} =$

11. $\dfrac{6}{9} + \dfrac{5}{9} =$

12. $\dfrac{1}{2} + \dfrac{2}{2} =$

13. $\dfrac{6}{8} + \dfrac{4}{8} =$

14. $\dfrac{9}{10} + \dfrac{3}{10} =$

15. $\dfrac{4}{5} + \dfrac{2}{5} =$

16. $\dfrac{8}{12} + \dfrac{7}{12} =$

First make the cut(s) on the models so the pieces are all the same size, rewrite one fraction, and then add the fractions.

1. $\dfrac{1}{6} + \dfrac{1}{3} =$

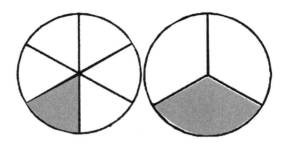

2. $\dfrac{3}{4} + \dfrac{1}{8} =$

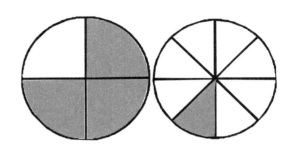

3. $\dfrac{1}{2} + \dfrac{1}{4} =$

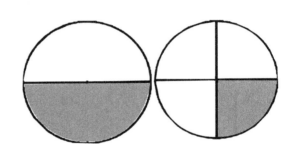

4. $\dfrac{1}{12} + \dfrac{1}{6} =$

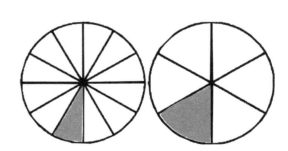

5. $\dfrac{2}{5} + \dfrac{3}{10} =$

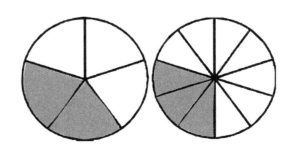

10-7 Adding fractions; change one denominator

Name_____

Add these fractions. You will need to change one denominator so that it matches the other one. Use your skills with equivalent fractions for this job! If you want to draw models, feel free. If you have an improper fraction as an answer, please simplify it.

1. $\dfrac{1}{4} + \dfrac{2}{8} =$

2. $\dfrac{1}{3} + \dfrac{3}{6} =$

3. $\dfrac{1}{4} + \dfrac{3}{8} =$

4. $\dfrac{2}{10} + \dfrac{2}{5} =$

5. $\dfrac{2}{6} + \dfrac{3}{12} =$

6. $\dfrac{1}{7} + \dfrac{4}{14} =$

7. $\dfrac{1}{4} + \dfrac{1}{2} =$

8. $\dfrac{1}{3} + \dfrac{2}{6} =$

9. $\dfrac{1}{3} + \dfrac{4}{6} =$

10. $\dfrac{3}{4} + \dfrac{3}{2} =$

11. $\dfrac{1}{4} + \dfrac{5}{8} =$

12. $\dfrac{1}{3} + \dfrac{5}{6} =$

13. $\dfrac{5}{8} + \dfrac{3}{4} =$

14. $\dfrac{4}{5} + \dfrac{3}{10} =$

15. $\dfrac{4}{12} + \dfrac{1}{6} =$

16. $\dfrac{2}{16} + \dfrac{1}{8} =$

10-8 Fraction ladders to make

Cut out the ladders. Use one ladder for each number. Leave the very first space empty, then start adding multiples of the numbers, putting one number on each rung of the ladder. Ex: for the first ladder: blank, 2, 4, 6, 8, 10, 12, etc.

10-9 Practicing with lowest common denominators

Name_____

For each pair of numbers, find one larger number they both go into. For example, 3 and 4 both go into 12 and 12 is the smallest number they both go into, so

1.   3 and 4

2.   2 and 3

3.   3 and 5

4.   2 and 5

5.   2 and 7

6.   3 and 7

7.   3 and 9

8.   4 and 5

9.   4 and 6

10. 5 and 6

11. 3 and 6

12. 3 and 8

13. 6 and 9

14. 4 and 5

15. 5 and 2

16. 5 and 3

10-10 Clock faces - fifteenths

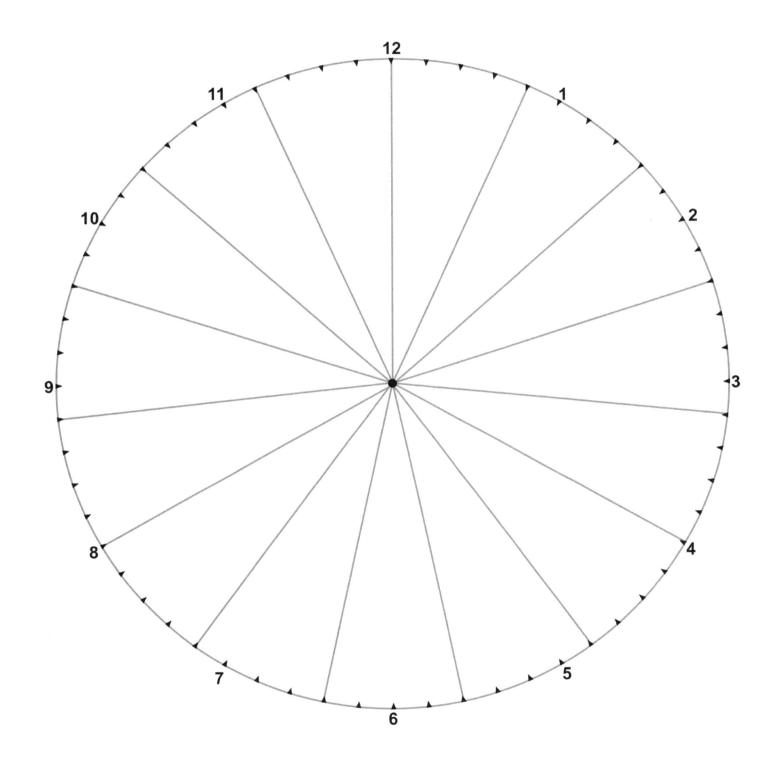

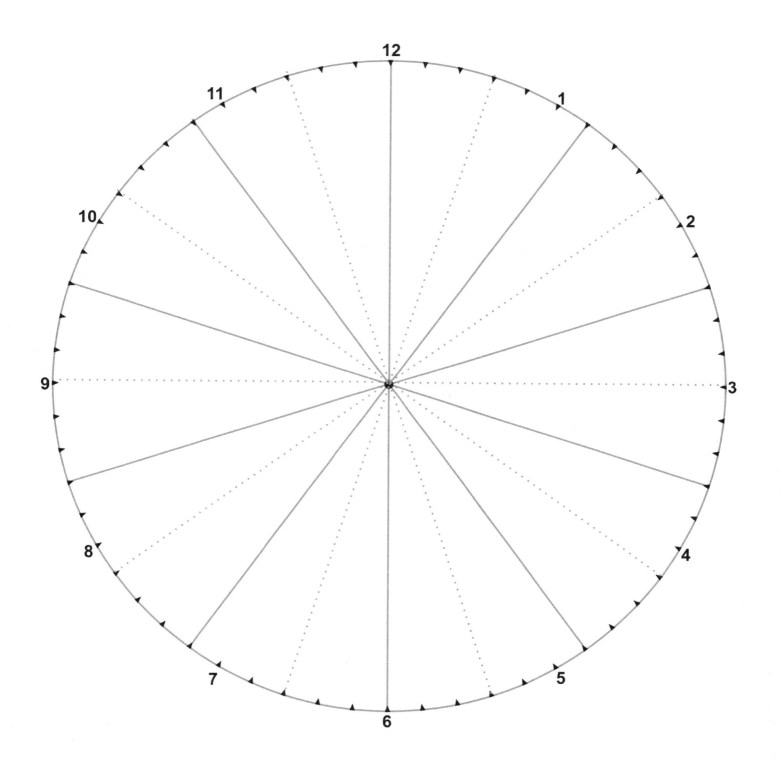

10-10 Clock faces - twenty-fourths

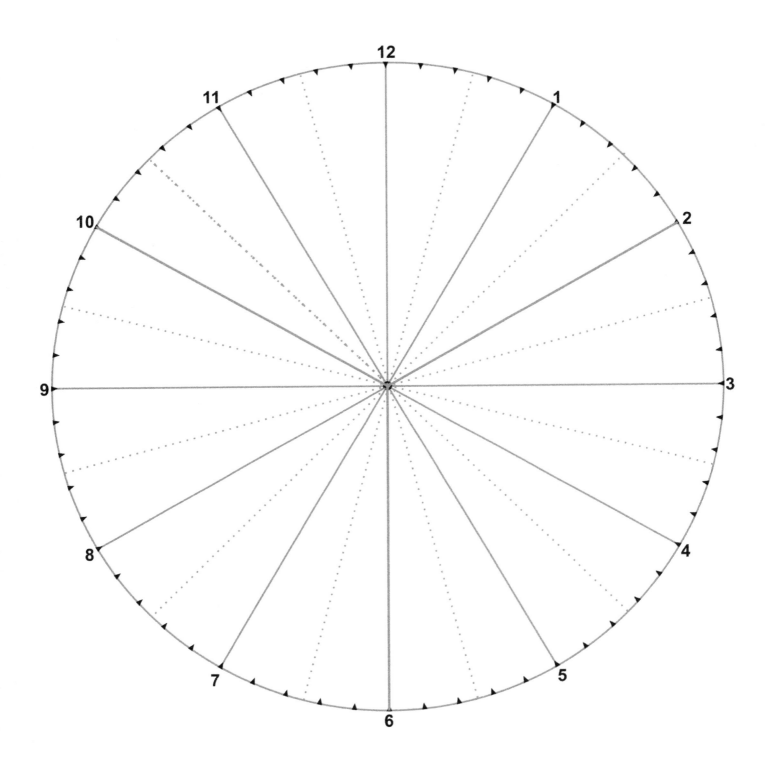

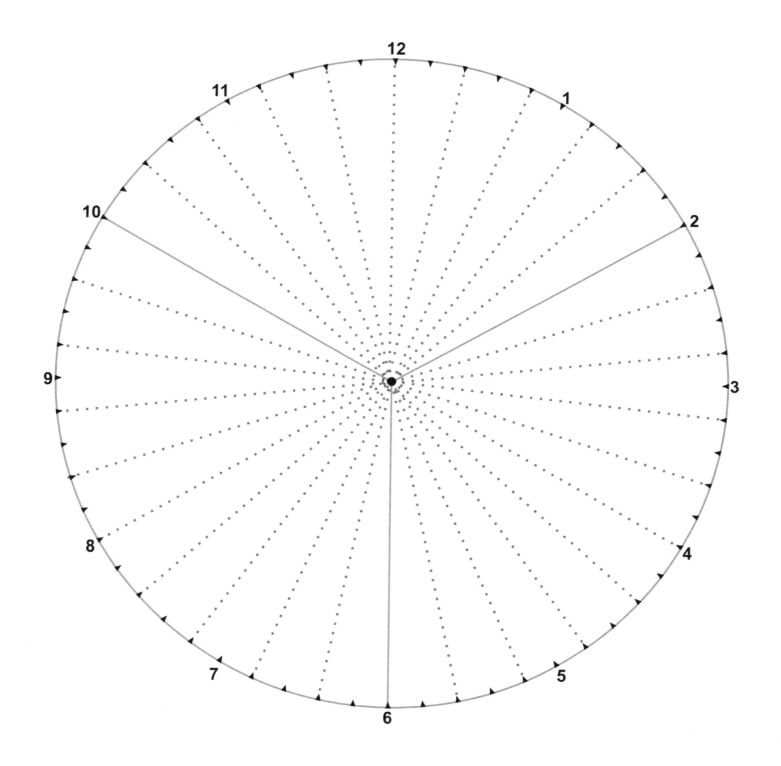

10-11 Adding fractions - rewriting both denominators

Name_____

Add the fractions below. You will need to rewrite each fraction first, so that the denominators are the same. The first one is started for you. Use your fraction ladders if you need to.

1.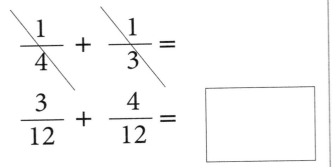

$$\frac{1}{4} + \frac{1}{3} =$$

$$\frac{3}{12} + \frac{4}{12} =$$

5. $$\frac{1}{3} + \frac{1}{2} =$$

2. $$\frac{1}{2} + \frac{1}{5} =$$

6. $$\frac{1}{7} + \frac{1}{2} =$$

3. $$\frac{1}{4} + \frac{1}{6} =$$

7. $$\frac{1}{3} + \frac{1}{5} =$$

4. $$\frac{1}{4} + \frac{1}{5} =$$

8. $$\frac{1}{9} + \frac{1}{6} =$$

156

10-12 Adding fractions rewriting both denominators

Name_____

Add the fractions below. You will need to rewrite each fraction first, so that the denominators are the same. The first one is started for you. Use your clock face or fraction strip models as needed.

1.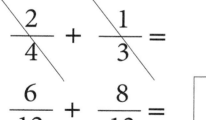
$$\frac{6}{12} + \frac{8}{12} =$$

2. $$\frac{1}{2} + \frac{3}{5} =$$

3. $$\frac{3}{4} + \frac{2}{6} =$$

4. $$\frac{1}{4} + \frac{2}{5} =$$

5. $$\frac{2}{3} + \frac{3}{2} =$$

6. $$\frac{2}{7} + \frac{1}{2} =$$

7. $$\frac{2}{3} + \frac{2}{5} =$$

8. $$\frac{1}{9} + \frac{3}{6} =$$

10-13 What I know about adding fractions

Name_____

Add the fractions below. Feel free to draw models or ladders for yourself as you work.

1. $\dfrac{1}{4} + \dfrac{2}{4} =$

2. $\dfrac{1}{3} + \dfrac{1}{3} =$

3. $\dfrac{3}{8} + \dfrac{4}{8} =$

4. $\dfrac{1}{5} + \dfrac{2}{5} =$

5. $\dfrac{3}{6} + \dfrac{2}{6} =$

6. $\dfrac{2}{4} + \dfrac{2}{4} =$

7. $\dfrac{4}{9} + \dfrac{2}{9} =$

8. $\dfrac{1}{3} + \dfrac{2}{3} =$

9. $\dfrac{3}{4} + \dfrac{2}{4} =$

10. $\dfrac{2}{3} + \dfrac{2}{3} =$

11. $\dfrac{7}{8} + \dfrac{4}{8} =$

12. $\dfrac{4}{5} + \dfrac{3}{5} =$

13. $\dfrac{1}{3} + \dfrac{4}{3} =$

14. $\dfrac{3}{4} + \dfrac{3}{4} =$

15. $\dfrac{6}{9} + \dfrac{5}{9} =$

16. $\dfrac{1}{2} + \dfrac{2}{2} =$

10-13 What I know about adding fractions

Name_____

Add the fractions below. Feel free to draw models or ladders for yourself as you work.

17. $\dfrac{1}{4} + \dfrac{2}{8} =$

18. $\dfrac{1}{3} + \dfrac{3}{6} =$

19. $\dfrac{1}{4} + \dfrac{3}{8} =$

20. $\dfrac{2}{10} + \dfrac{2}{5} =$

21. $\dfrac{1}{3} + \dfrac{4}{6} =$

22. $\dfrac{3}{4} + \dfrac{3}{2} =$

23. $\dfrac{1}{4} + \dfrac{5}{8} =$

24. $\dfrac{1}{3} + \dfrac{5}{6} =$

25. $\dfrac{1}{2} + \dfrac{1}{5} =$

26. $\dfrac{1}{4} + \dfrac{1}{6} =$

27. $\dfrac{1}{4} + \dfrac{1}{5} =$

28. $\dfrac{1}{7} + \dfrac{1}{2} =$

29. $\dfrac{1}{3} + \dfrac{1}{5} =$

30. $\dfrac{1}{3} + \dfrac{1}{4} =$

11 ADDING MIXED NUMBERS

Goals for This Chapter:
1. Adding mixed numbers with like denominators
2. Adding mixed numbers, changing one denominator
3. Adding mixed numbers, changing both denominators

I. Adding mixed numbers with like denominators

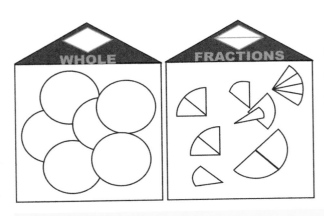

Adding mixed numbers can be difficult for some students, so let's make it as kid-friendly as possible! Let's ground the action of adding mixed numbers in story and image.

Num and Nom had been making pizza for months. The pizza had gotten better and better tasting, and more and more people just happened to drop by their house when they were baking, hoping to sample the fresh pizza! One day, Num looked at Nom and said, "We are baking so much pizza, so many people are coming over to eat, we might as well open a pizza shop!"

"Brilliant!" said Nom. "Let's do it!" So the brothers opened a pizza shop and advertised in the paper. Before long they had a booming business! People lined up around the block to get their hands on some delicious, piping hot pizza!

Each morning the brothers baked, and then as Nom cut slices, Num loaded the pizzas into their little storage ovens to keep warm. Some customers came in the shop and bought whole pizzas, but other customers bought pizza by the slice. Num soon decided to store the pans with missing slices in a separate warming oven. He labeled one oven "WHOLE" and the other "FRACTIONS."

During the day, as the brothers sold pizza, they baked more. The whole pizzas went into the "WHOLE" warming oven, and the slices were added to the "FRACTIONS" warming oven.

The very process of adding more pizza to warming ovens mimics the action of adding mixed numbers. Whole numbers will go into the left, added to the ones that are already there. The individual slices or fractions of pizzas will go to the right. Of course, as Nom adds slices to the FRACTIONS warming oven, he will monitor what is in there. If he creates a new whole from the slices he puts into the warming oven, that new whole pizza will need to be moved to the left into the WHOLE warming oven.

Let's get the students involved in an activity now.

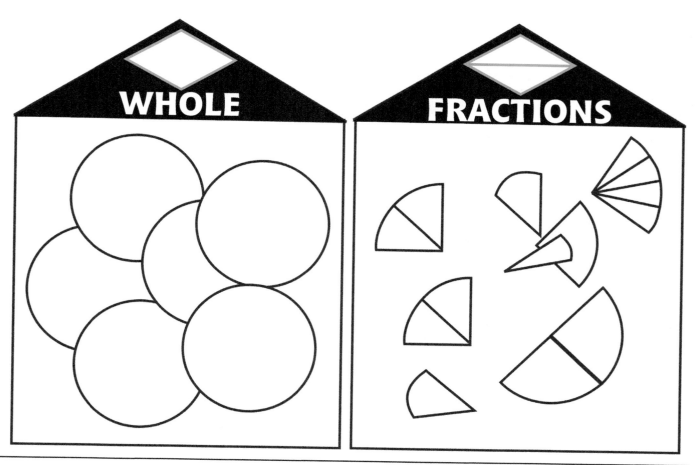

Hands On:

Use Resource 11-1 to give students practice with adding mixed numbers.

1. **Add 1 1/4 + 3 2/4**

    a. First add the whole numbers and put them in the whole warming oven. [4]

    b. Next add the two fractions and put their sum in the fractions oven.   [3/4]

2. **Add 1 3/6 + 2 2/6**

    a. First add the whole numbers and put them in WHOLE.   [3]

    b. Next add the two fractions and put their sum in FRACTIONS.   [5/6]

If you feel your students don't need help, let them complete Resource 11-1 on their own.

II. Adding fractions that equal more than a whole

This next section will be handled just the same as the first section, but this time when students add the fractions, they will have more than a whole. When this happens, the improper fraction cannot stay in FRACTIONS! The students will make a whole out of the improper fraction and then store the whole where it belongs. Depending on your students' needs, use fraction models to add the fractions, make a whole and see what is happening.

Hands On:
Use Resource 11-2 to give students practice with making and moving a whole.

1. **Add 3/4 + 3/4**

   a. Add Nums [6/4]

   b. Take a whole (4/4) from 6/4.

   c. Write the 1 (whole) in WHOLE and the left overs in FRACTIONS [2/4]. [=1 2/4].

2. **Add 2/3 + 4/3**

   a. Add Nums [6/3]

   b. Take a whole (3/3) from 6/3.

   c. Write the 1 (whole) in WHOLE and the left overs in FRACTIONS [3/3].

   d. Uh Oh! We have another whole! 3/3 is the same as 1, so we need to add it to WHOLE [2].

3. **Add 2/5 + 4/5**

   a. Add Nums [6/5]

   b. Take a whole (5/5) from 6/5.

   c. Write the 1 (whole) in WHOLE and the left overs in FRACTIONS [1/5]. [=1 1/5].

Let the students continue on their own as soon as you feel they are able to do so.

III. Adding mixed numbers when fractions make a whole

I would encourage the students to draw simple pictures to show the action of solving the problems in this section. Alternately they can work with a partner and use fraction models.

Hands On:
Use Resource 11-3 to give students practice with adding mixed numbers that require making and moving a whole.

Look at the problem 1 3/4 + 2 2/4 on Resource 11-3. Here are the steps to solve:

   a. Draw circles to represent the whole numbers. Put the sum in the whole numbers oven [3]

   b. Add the fractions and put that sum in the fractions oven [3/4 + 2/4 = 5/4].

   c. Now, we need to look at FRACTIONS to see if we can make a whole. [5/4 - 4/4 = 1/4]

d. We will move the new whole to WHOLE and add it to the numbers there [4].

e. Finally, we will write the left over fraction in FRACTIONS [1/4].

f. Our answer is 4 1/4

I would recommend talking with the students as you work so they can hear your own thoughts as you solve problems with them, and also encourage them to talk about what they are doing as they solve problems. It would be great if you could give each student a chance to lead in solving a problem, explaining the process to the group.

IV. Adding mixed numbers, changing one denominator

If you feel you need to, do a quick review of this process from Chapter 10 (Resource 10-6). It would also be good to review the activity where the students identify a lowest common denominator for pairs of fractions. (Resource 10-9).

Using our warming ovens idea again, let's do some practice addition together.

1. **Add** 1 1/3 + 2 2/6.

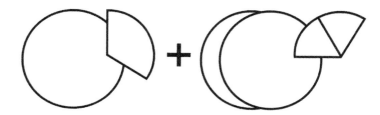

Ask: "What should we do first?" Students might say to add the wholes and write a 3 in WHOLE. Or they might want to deal with the fractions first. Either option is correct. If we add the whole numbers first, this is what we'd have: 3 wholes, 1/3, and 2/6 like this:

Ask: "What do we need to do to the fractions so we can add them?" [We will need to cut the 1/3 in half to make sixths so we can add 2/6 + 2/6.]

For the next few problems, encourage the students to draw little models for themselves. (I was still drawing models for myself when I was in graduate school!)

Hands On:
Use Resource 11-4 to give students practice with adding mixed numbers that require changing one denominator to match the other.

V. Adding mixed numbers changing two denominators

Let the students use their LCD ladders they made for Chapter 10 as needed. Provide a lot of practice in this section so that students will become very comfortable with the process. Ask the students to think about what will help them the most and let them use their own best tools so they can be successful.

Let's do some practice together.

1. **Add 1 1/4 + 2 1/3.**

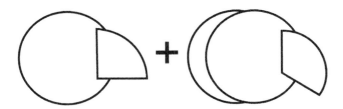

a. Add 1+2 wholes. [3].

b. Now we have 1/4 and 1/3. What is the LCD? [12]

c. How many 12ths are in 1/4? [3].

d. How many 12ths are in 1/3? [4].

e. Now this is what we have once we've cut the fractions into 12ths: [1 1/4 + 2 1/3 = 3 7/12].

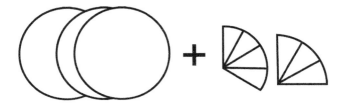

2. **Add 2 1/3 + 1/ 1/2.**

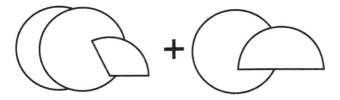

a. Add the wholes [3].

b. What is the LCD for 1/3 and 1/2? [6]

c. How many sixths in 1/3? [2]

d. How many sixths in 1/2? [3]

e. This is what we have when we've cut the fractions into sixths: [2 1/3 + 1 1/2 = 3 5/6].

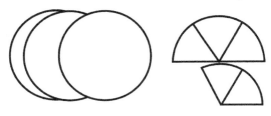

Hands On:

Use Resource 11-5 to give students practice with adding mixed numbers that require changing both denominators.

VI. Adding mixed numbers, LCD, making a whole

Now we're really ramping up our process, so please be sure the students are comfortable with adding the problems they have had so far. Now we will be adding one more element: that of making a whole and transfering it to WHOLES.

Hands On:

Use Resource 11-6 to give students practice with adding mixed numbers that require changing both denominators as well as making and transferring a whole.

1. **Add 1 3/4 + 2 1/3.**

Ask the students to draw models for themselves like we did in the last section. (To make fourths, you draw a line from top to bottom and from side to side. To draw thirds, start in the middle of the circle and draw a line straight down. Next, draw lines from the center of the circle to the spots where 10 o'clock and 2 o'clock would be on a clock face.)

a. Add the wholes [3]

b. Find the LCD for fourths and thirds [12]

c. How many 12ths are in fourths? [3] Divide the fourths into 12ths.

d. How many 12ths are in thirds? [4] Divide the third into 12ths.

e. Add 9/12 + 4/12. [13/12]

f. Because we have more than a whole, we need to move a whole to WHOLE. Now we have 4 wholes and 1/12 left over in FRACTIONS. [4 1/12].

2. **Add 1 2/3 + 1 1/2.**

Ask the students to draw models for themselves.

a. Add the wholes [2]

b. Find the LCD for halves and thirds [6]

c. How many 6ths are in 1/2? [3] Divide the 1/2 into 3 pieces.

d. How many 6ths are in thirds? [2] Divide each third into 2 pieces [4 pieces total].

e. Add 4/6 + 3/6 [7/6].

f. Because we have more than a whole, we need to move a whole to WHOLE. Now we have 3 wholes and 1/6 left over in FRACTIONS. [3 1/6].

Complete Resource 11-6. If your students need more practice, use Resouce 11-7. At every point, check for a student who might be overwhelmed. For those students, rather than repeating steps verbally, let them work out the steps logically using models. The things they write on paper should reflect closely what they have done in tactile activities.

Finally, when your students are comfortable with adding mixed numbers, give them the assessment using Resource 11-8.

NOTE: To some students it might make more sense to work with fractions first and then add the wholes. Remember that the most important thing that we can offer our students is the ability to think for themselves about what makes the most sense. Ask them frequently what makes the most sense to them. How would they choose to solve the problem? If one way makes sense to them but we tell them they have to do it our way, it will make it harder for the student to become fluent and natural with the process.

11-1 Adding mixed numbers with like denominators

Name_____

Add the fractions and write the answers. Put the whole numbers to the left and the fractions to the right.

1. $1\frac{1}{4}$
$+ 3\frac{2}{4}$

2. $1\frac{3}{6}$
$+ 2\frac{2}{6}$

3. $1\frac{1}{3}$
$+ 3\frac{1}{3}$

4. $3\frac{4}{10}$
$+ 6\frac{3}{10}$

5. $2\frac{1}{4}$
$+ 2\frac{1}{4}$

6. $2\frac{3}{8}$
$+ 3\frac{4}{8}$

7. $2\frac{4}{9}$
$+ 1\frac{2}{9}$

8. $2\frac{2}{9}$
$+ 2\frac{3}{9}$

9. $2\frac{1}{5}$
$+ 2\frac{2}{5}$

10. $2\frac{1}{3}$
$+ 1\frac{1}{3}$

11. $1\frac{1}{6}$
$+ 2\frac{4}{6}$

12. $2\frac{3}{5}$
$+ 3\frac{1}{5}$

13. $3\frac{2}{8}$
$+ 1\frac{5}{8}$

14. $2\frac{2}{7}$
$+ 5\frac{3}{7}$

15. $3\frac{4}{7}$
$+ 2\frac{1}{7}$

11-2 Adding fractions that make a whole and more

Name_____

Add these fractions. They will each make more than one whole. Put the whole into the whole number oven and the fraction to the right.

1. $\dfrac{3}{4} + \dfrac{3}{4} =$

2. $\dfrac{2}{3} + \dfrac{4}{3} =$

3. $\dfrac{2}{5} + \dfrac{4}{5} =$

4. $\dfrac{1}{2} + \dfrac{1}{2} =$

5. $\dfrac{5}{8} + \dfrac{7}{8} =$

6. $\dfrac{6}{9} + \dfrac{7}{9} =$

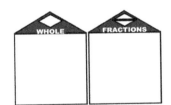

7. $\dfrac{4}{5} + \dfrac{3}{5} =$

8. $\dfrac{2}{3} + \dfrac{2}{3} =$

9. $\dfrac{5}{6} + \dfrac{4}{6} =$

10. $\dfrac{7}{8} + \dfrac{7}{8} =$

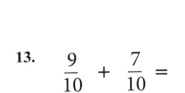

11. $\dfrac{5}{7} + \dfrac{4}{7} =$

12. $\dfrac{6}{7} + \dfrac{3}{7} =$

13. $\dfrac{9}{10} + \dfrac{7}{10} =$

14. $\dfrac{6}{9} + \dfrac{5}{9} =$

15. $\dfrac{4}{5} + \dfrac{2}{5} =$

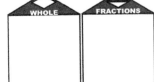

Add whole numbers, add fractions, simplify, move the whole to WHOLE side, write the fraction in FRACTIONS side.

1. $1\frac{3}{4}$

$+ 2\frac{2}{4}$

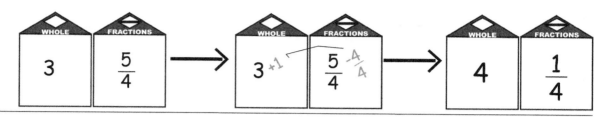

2. $2\frac{3}{4}$

$+ 1\frac{1}{4}$

3. $2\frac{5}{8}$

$+ 1\frac{4}{8}$

4. $3\frac{4}{9}$

$+ 1\frac{7}{9}$

5. $2\frac{4}{5}$

$+ 2\frac{2}{5}$

6. $2\frac{2}{3}$

$+ 1\frac{2}{3}$

7. $1\frac{4}{6}$

$+ 2\frac{4}{6}$

8. $3\frac{7}{8}$

$+ 1\frac{5}{8}$

9. $2\frac{5}{7}$

$+ 2\frac{3}{7}$

10. $1\frac{6}{7}$

$+ 2\frac{3}{7}$

11-4 Adding mixed numbers; change one denominator

Add. You will need to change one Nom to make it the same is the other one.

1. $1 \frac{3}{8}$
$+2 \frac{1}{4}$

2. $1 \frac{3}{6}$
$+2 \frac{1}{3}$

3. $1 \frac{1}{4}$
$+2 \frac{1}{2}$

4. $2 \frac{3}{8}$
$+2 \frac{1}{4}$

5. $2 \frac{1}{4}$
$+1 \frac{4}{8}$

6. $3 \frac{2}{5}$
$+1 \frac{3}{10}$

7. $2 \frac{1}{2}$
$+1 \frac{1}{4}$

8. $1 \frac{1}{3}$
$+2 \frac{2}{6}$

9. $3 \frac{2}{8}$
$+1 \frac{1}{4}$

10. $2 \frac{1}{5}$
$+1 \frac{7}{10}$

11. $1 \frac{1}{6}$
$+2 \frac{5}{12}$

12. $3 \frac{1}{2}$
$+1 \frac{2}{4}$

11-5 Adding mixed numbers changing both denominators

Name_____

Add. You will need to change Noms so they are the same.

1. $1\frac{1}{2}$
$+2\frac{1}{3}$

2. $1\frac{1}{3}$
$+2\frac{1}{4}$

3. $1\frac{1}{2}$
$+2\frac{2}{5}$

4. $1\frac{1}{3}$
$+1\frac{1}{4}$

5. $2\frac{1}{3}$
$+1\frac{2}{5}$

6. $3\frac{1}{4}$
$+1\frac{1}{5}$

7. $2\frac{2}{4}$
$+1\frac{1}{3}$

8. $1\frac{3}{5}$
$+2\frac{1}{2}$

9. $2\frac{2}{7}$
$+1\frac{1}{2}$

10. $2\frac{1}{5}$
$+1\frac{2}{3}$

11. $1\frac{2}{3}$
$+2\frac{1}{2}$

12. $3\frac{1}{2}$
$+1\frac{1}{5}$

11-6 Adding mixed numbers changing both denominators   Name_____

Add. You will need to change both Noms so they are the same. You will also need to make and move a whole.

1. $2\frac{1}{2}$
$+1\frac{2}{3}$

2. $1\frac{1}{2}$
$+2\frac{1}{7}$

3. $1\frac{1}{2}$
$+3\frac{3}{5}$

4. $2\frac{2}{3}$
$+1\frac{3}{4}$

5. $2\frac{1}{3}$
$+1\frac{4}{5}$

6. $3\frac{3}{4}$
$+1\frac{2}{5}$

7. $2\frac{3}{4}$
$+1\frac{1}{3}$

8. $1\frac{4}{5}$
$+2\frac{1}{2}$

9. $2\frac{6}{7}$
$+1\frac{1}{2}$

10. $2\frac{3}{5}$
$+1\frac{2}{3}$

11. $1\frac{2}{3}$
$+2\frac{1}{2}$

12. $1\frac{2}{3}$
$+1\frac{1}{4}$

11-7 Adding mixed numbers

Add, making sure to check denominators. You might need to make and move a whole.

1. $2\frac{3}{4}$
    $+3\frac{2}{3}$

2. $2\frac{3}{2}$
    $+2\frac{1}{6}$

3. $1\frac{2}{2}$
    $+3\frac{4}{5}$

4. $2\frac{2}{3}$
    $+2\frac{7}{12}$

5. $2\frac{3}{4}$
    $+4\frac{4}{5}$

6. $3\frac{3}{4}$
    $+1\frac{1}{2}$

7. $3\frac{2}{6}$
    $+4\frac{3}{4}$

8. $1\frac{7}{10}$
    $+2\frac{1}{2}$

9. $2\frac{6}{7}$
    $+1\frac{2}{3}$

10. $2\frac{4}{5}$
    $+1\frac{1}{2}$

11. $1\frac{5}{6}$
    $+2\frac{1}{3}$

12. $3\frac{1}{3}$
    $+1\frac{7}{10}$

11-8 Let me show you what I know about adding mixed numbers!   Name_____

Add. You are so good at this now!

1. $1\frac{1}{4}$
    $+3\frac{2}{4}$

2. $1\frac{3}{6}$
    $+2\frac{2}{6}$

3. $1\frac{1}{3}$
    $+3\frac{1}{3}$

4. $2\frac{3}{8}$
    $+1\frac{1}{4}$

5. $2\frac{1}{4}$
    $+1\frac{4}{8}$

6. $3\frac{2}{5}$
    $+1\frac{3}{10}$

7. $2\frac{2}{4}$
    $+1\frac{1}{3}$

8. $1\frac{3}{5}$
    $+2\frac{1}{2}$

9. $2\frac{2}{7}$
    $+1\frac{1}{2}$

10. $2\frac{3}{5}$
    $+1\frac{2}{3}$

11. $1\frac{4}{6}$
    $+2\frac{1}{2}$

12. $3\frac{2}{3}$
    $+1\frac{7}{9}$

13. $3\frac{1}{2}$
    $+2\frac{5}{8}$

14. $2\frac{6}{7}$
    $+4\frac{1}{2}$

15. $1\frac{5}{6}$
    $+2\frac{1}{2}$

SUBTRACTING FRACTIONS

Goals for This Chapter:

1. Subtracting fractions with like denominators
2. Subtracting fractions, changing one denominator
3. Subtracting fractions, changing both denominators

I. Subtracting fractions with like denominators

The really good news about subtracting fractions with like denominators is that if we know how to add that kind of fraction, subtracting is just the same thing but going backwards. Because many students tend to have a mental block against subtraction, have them work through this process with you using models.

Let's solve 4/8 + 3/8. First ask your students to use the fraction strip for eighths.

1. Cover 3/8 with their pencils or a finger and then cover 4/8 more.

Ask: "How many 1/8 did you cover in all?" [7/8]

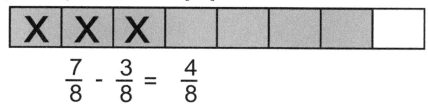

$$\frac{7}{8} - \frac{3}{8} = \frac{4}{8}$$

2. Now have the students fold under 1/8 on their fraction strip, leaving 7/8 showing.

Ask: "How much is 7/8 - 3/8?" They will need to fold under 3/8 more. This will leave 4/8 showing.

$$\frac{7}{8} - \frac{3}{8} = \frac{4}{8}$$

Let's do the same problem again, but this time with clock faces.

1. Let's add 3/8 and 4/8. It is easy to see the answer is 7/8.

2. Now let's subtract 7/8 - 3/8. If the students start out with 7 eighths pieces on their 8s clock face and then subtract 3 of them, they will have 4 left over.

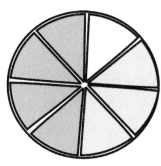

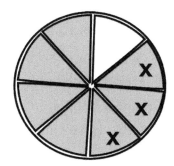

$$\frac{4}{8} + \frac{3}{8} = \frac{7}{8} \qquad \frac{7}{8} - \frac{3}{8} = \frac{4}{8}$$

We can also use set models to solve the same problem of 7/8 - 3/8. First students will draw a circle and then draw 8 little circles inside the larger one. They will color in 7 of the circles to represent 7/8.

Next, they will mark 3 of the eighths with an X showing that they have been subtracted. [4/8].

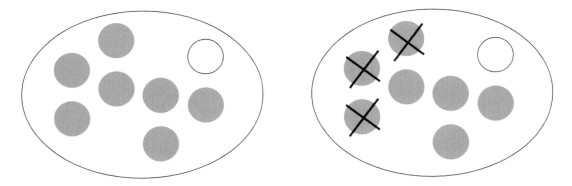

Let's do another problem together with students drawing a model for their work. Let's subtract 3/4 - 1/4. Students will draw a circle or a square. Next they will draw lines that cut the whole into fourths. They will color three of the fourths to make 3/4. Next, they will draw an X over 1/4. [2/4].

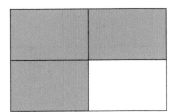 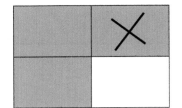

Hands On:
Use Resource 12-1. Subtracting fractions with like denominators.

II. Subtracting mixed numbers; same denominators

In this section, students will need to create improper fractions in order to subtract. Have them use their clockface models or the strips for this exercise.

1. **Subtract 1 3/8 - 4/8.**

   a. **Ask** "Can we subtract 4/8 from 3/8? [No].

   b. Model for the students changing the mixed number into an improper fraction so it is ready to subtract from. 1 is the same as 8/8. If they are using a model for this, they will need a whole plus 3 eighths sections. Or they can draw the problem. They will have a circle with 8 small circles inside of it plus three small circles beside that.

   c. 8/8 + 3/8 = 11/8. Now the problem is 11/8 - 4/8 = 7/8. They can X off 4 eighths to solve.

2. **Subtract 1 3/5 - 4/5.**

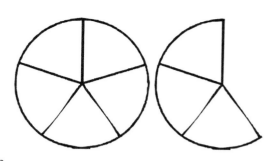

a. **Ask** "Can we subtract 4/5 from 3/5? [No].

b. Model for the students changing the mixed number into an improper fraction so it is ready to subtract from. 1 is the same as 5/5. If they are using a model for this, they will need a whole plus 3 fifths sections. Or they can draw the problem. They will have a circle with 5 small circles inside of it plus three small circles beside that.

c. 5/5 + 3/5 = 8/5. Now the problem is 8/5 - 4/5 = 4/5. They can X off 4 fifths to solve.

Hands On:

Use Resource 12-2 Subtracting mixed numbers with like denominators.

III. Subtracting mixed numbers; change one denominator

By way of review, let's do some mental LCD work. Challenge the students to see these combinations in their minds as already converted to same denominators. Write the problems on your whiteboard and talk your way through them with the students:

1. 1/3 + 1/6   [Double 1, double 3 = 2/6.   2/6 + 1/6 = 3/6].
2. 4/5 + 3/10   [Double 4, double 5 = 8/10.   8/10 + 3/10 = 11/10 or 1 1/10].
3. 1/2 + 1/4   [Double 1, double 2 = 2/4.   2/4 + 1/4 = 3/4].
4. 2/6 + 3/12   [Double 2, double 6 = 4/12.   4/12 + 3/12 = 7/12].

Next, we can create subtraction problems in which we change one denominator so that it matches the other. Again, use your whiteboard to walk through the problems, but this time, have the students use scratch paper to draw little models for each problem

1. **1 1/3 - 5/6.**

a. Rewrite the first mixed number into an improper fraction [3/3 + 1/3 = 4/3]. Draw a circle with three little circles inside. Draw 1 small circle beside it. This shows 4/3.

b. Rewrite the improper fraction so that its denominator matches 1/6. [4/3 = 8/6]. Show this by cutting in half each of the four little circles. Now you have 8 sixths.

c. Rewrite the original problem now: 8/6 - 5/6 = 3/6. Draw an X over 5 of the sixths.

2. **1 4/5 - 9/10.**

a. Rewrite the first mixed number [5/5 + 4/5 = 9/5]. Draw a circle with 5 little circles inside. Draw 4 small circles beside it. This shows 9/5.

b. Rewrite the improper fraction so that its denominator is10. [9/5 = 18/10]. Show this by cutting in half each of the 9 little circles. Now you have 18 tenths.

c. Rewrite the original problem now: 18/10 - 9/10 = 9/10. Draw an X over 9 of the tenths. [9/10].

Continue by doing two more problems together in the same manner before turning the students loose on Resource 12-3.

3. **2 1/2 - 3/4**   [2 1/2 = 4/4 + 4/4 + 2/4 or 10/4.   10/4 - 3/4 = 7/4 or 1 3/4]

4. **1 1/6 - 7/12**   [1 1/6 = 12/12 + 2/12 = 14/12.   14/12 - 7/12 = 7/12]

 Hands On:
Use Resource 12-3 Subtracting mixed numbers; change one denominator.

IV. Subtracting fractions; change both denominators

For this section, students will use their clock faces from Chapter 10, Resource 10-10. They can use their ladders also, as they find LCD. They might prefer fraction strips to clock faces. Let them choose their models. Remember, the right way to solve problems is what makes the most sense to each student. Also, use the visual on the next page to review the process of finding LCD.

1. **3/4 - 1/3**

   a. Find the LCD first, using any means that is comfortable to each student.   [12]

   b. Take the 12s clockface and lay 3 fourths on top of it. How many 12ths is 3/4?   [9/12].

   (3 x 4 = 12 (Nom) and 3 x 3 = 9 (Num)).

   c. Lay 1 third on top of the 3/4 models, making sure one edge lines up. How many 12ths is 1/3?

   [4/12]   (4 x 3 = 12 (Nom) and 4 x 1 = 4 (Num)).

   d. When you subtract 9/12 - 4/12, how many 12ths are left? [5/12].

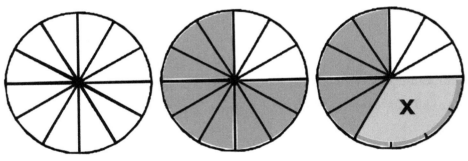

   12ths clockface   *3/4 on the clockface*   *minus 1/3 or 4/12*

2. **7/8 - 2/3**

   a. Find the LCD first, using any means that is comfortable to each student.   [24]

   b. Take the 24ths clockface and cover 7 eighths. How many 24ths is that?   [21/24]

   c. Cover the clockface with 2/3, making sure to match edges with the 7/8.

   How many 24ths is 2/3?   [16/24]

   d. When you subtract 21/24 - 16/24, how many 24ths are left? [5/24].

Continue to work problems together until you feel your students are ready to work on their own. Use:

1/2 - 2/5 [5/10 - 4/10 = 1/10]   1/2 - 1/3 [3/6 - 2/6 = 1/6]   2/3 - 1/4 [8/12 - 3/12 = 5/12]

3/4 - 2/5 [15/20 - 8/20 = 7/20]   4/5 - 1/3 [12/15 - 5/15 = 7/15].

Here is a visual of the process of finding lowest common denominator.

PROBLEM: Subtract: 1/3 - 1/5

- Put 3 and 5 on the bottom rungs and add multiples of those numbers on the ladders
- Find the lowest (smallest) number they both have in common [15]
- Multiply each fraction by the number of rungs you climbed to find the LCD
- Rewrite the fractions and then subtract

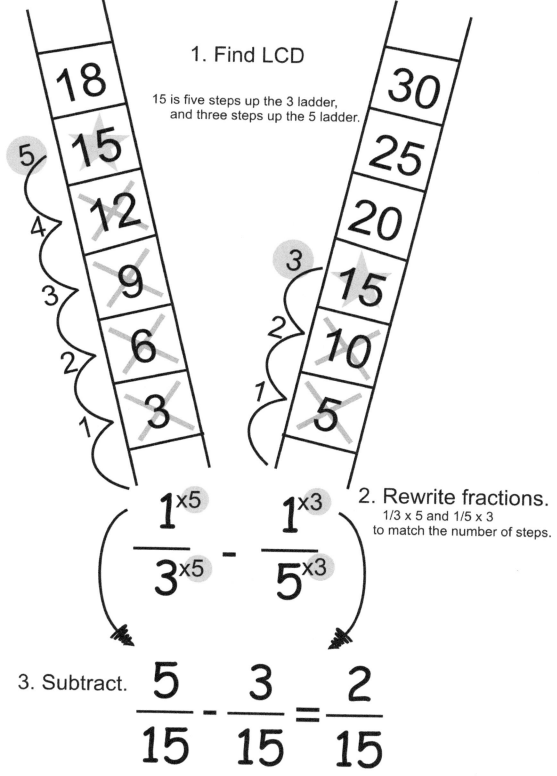

1. Find LCD

15 is five steps up the 3 ladder, and three steps up the 5 ladder.

2. Rewrite fractions.
1/3 x 5 and 1/5 x 3
to match the number of steps.

3. Subtract. $\dfrac{5}{15} - \dfrac{3}{15} = \dfrac{2}{15}$

V. Subtracting mixed numbers; change both denominators

At this stage in the game, it will be important for you as the teacher to fully understand where each of your students are in terms of :

1. Ease in finding LCD including what LCD means (give your students a copy of the visual on the next page as desired so they will have a reminder of the procedure).

2. Relating the process of cutting model pieces to finding LCD for two fractions.

3. Knowing what each student finds to be most helpful as they are computing. Is it sketching models for themselves? Is it referring to images provided in this book? Is it using fraction models? Or do they have the concepts down pat by now?

To find the answers to these questions, discuss with your students, asking them to share with you their thinking.

Practice problems:

1. **Solve 2 1/2 - 1 1/3. Here is the model.**

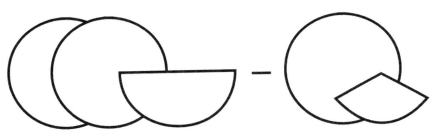

In this problem, seeing the visual model of the various pieces, it become obvious that you can subtract 1 whole from 2 wholes and you can subtract 1/3 from 1/2 (once you have Lowest Common Denominators).

a. Find LCD for 1/2 and 1/3 [6].
b. Rewrite the fractions. [1/2 = 3/6 and 1/3 = 2/6]
c. Now we can easily subtract: 2 - 1 = 1 and 3/6 - 2/6 = 1/6

$$2 \frac{1}{2} \frac{3}{6}$$
$$-1 \frac{1}{3} \frac{2}{6}$$

2. **Solve 2 1/3 - 1 1/5. Draw a model.**

a. Find LCD for 1/3 and 1/5 [15].
b. Rewrite the fractions. 1/3 = 5/15 and 1/5 = 3/15.
c. Now we can easily subtract 2 - 1 = 1 and 5/15 - 3/15 = 2/15.

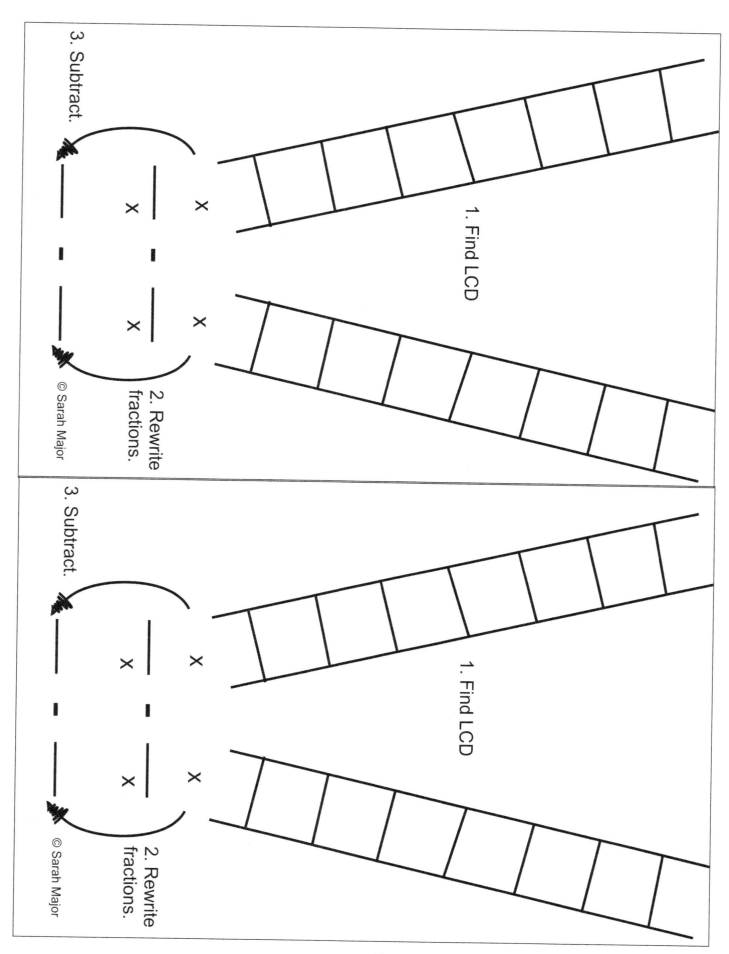

3. Subtract.

2. Rewrite fractions.

1. Find LCD

© Sarah Major

3. Subtract.

2. Rewrite fractions.

1. Find LCD

© Sarah Major

181

3. **Solve 2 1/2 - 1 2/3. Draw a model.**

    a. Find LCD for 1/2 and 2/3 [6].

    b. Rewrite the fractions. [1/2 = 3/6 and 2/3 = 4/6.]

    c. Ask: "Can we subtract 4/6 from 3/6? [No.]

    d. We will need to make improper fractions before we can subtract.

    e. 2 3/6 = 6/6 + 6/6 + 3/6 = 15/6   and   1 4/6 = 6/6 + 4/6 = 10/6

    f. Subtract: 15/6 - 10/6 = 5/6.

This problem shows us how being able to estimate fractions comes in handy. If we look at the fractions and can see that the first fraction is smaller than the second one, then we will know we need to make an improper fraction before subtracting.

If, however, the second mixed number contains a fraction smaller than the first, all we need to do is find the LCD before we subtract.

Do these problems together:

1. **Solve 1 2/3 - 1 1/4.**

    a. LCD is 12

    b. 2/3 = 8/12

    c. 1/4 = 3/12

    d. 1 8/12 - 1 3/12 = 5/12.

2. **Solve 3 1/2 - 1 2/5.**

    a. LCD is 10

    b. 1/2 = 5/10

    c. 2/5 = 4/10

    d. 3 5/10 - 1 4/10 = 2 1/10.

3. **Solve 1 1/4 - 2/3.**

    a. LCD is 12

    b. 1 1/4 = 12/12 + 3/12 or 15/12

    c. 2/3 = 8/12

    d. 15/12 - 8/12 = 7/12.

Hands On:
    Use Resource 12-5. Subtracting mixed numbers, changing both denominators.

Finally, assess them using Resource 12-6. Go over any area you feel is troublesome as needed, making sure to use hands-on activities to help.

12-1 Subtracting fractions with like denominators

Name_____

Subtract mixed numbers.

1. $\dfrac{3}{4}$ $-\dfrac{2}{4}$

2. $\dfrac{3}{6}$ $-\dfrac{2}{6}$

3. $\dfrac{2}{3}$ $-\dfrac{1}{3}$

4. $\dfrac{4}{10}$ $-\dfrac{3}{10}$

5. $\dfrac{3}{4}$ $-\dfrac{1}{4}$

6. $\dfrac{7}{8}$ $-\dfrac{4}{8}$

7. $\dfrac{4}{9}$ $-\dfrac{2}{9}$

8. $\dfrac{8}{9}$ $-\dfrac{3}{9}$

9. $\dfrac{4}{5}$ $-\dfrac{2}{5}$

10. $\dfrac{2}{3}$ $-\dfrac{1}{3}$

11. $\dfrac{5}{6}$ $-\dfrac{1}{6}$

12. $\dfrac{4}{5}$ $-\dfrac{1}{5}$

13. $\dfrac{7}{8}$ $-\dfrac{5}{8}$

14. $\dfrac{5}{7}$ $-\dfrac{3}{7}$

15. $\dfrac{4}{7}$ $-\dfrac{1}{7}$

12-2 Subtracting mixed numbers with like denominators

Name_____

Subtract mixed numbers.

1. $2\dfrac{1}{3}$
$-\ 1\dfrac{2}{3}$

2. $2\dfrac{1}{6}$
$-\ 1\dfrac{2}{6}$

3. $3\dfrac{1}{4}$
$-\ 2\dfrac{2}{4}$

4. $2\dfrac{1}{5}$
$-\ 1\dfrac{2}{5}$

5. $2\dfrac{1}{4}$
$-\ 1\dfrac{3}{4}$

6. $2\dfrac{3}{8}$
$-\ 1\dfrac{4}{8}$

7. $2\dfrac{1}{9}$
$-\ 1\dfrac{2}{9}$

8. $2\dfrac{3}{6}$
$-\ 2\dfrac{1}{6}$

9. $2\dfrac{1}{5}$
$-\ 1\dfrac{3}{5}$

10. $2\dfrac{1}{3}$
$-\ 1\dfrac{2}{3}$

11. $4\dfrac{1}{4}$
$-\ 2\dfrac{3}{4}$

12. $2\dfrac{2}{5}$
$-\ 1\dfrac{4}{5}$

13. $2\dfrac{1}{8}$
$-\ 1\dfrac{7}{8}$

14. $3\dfrac{3}{7}$
$-\ 2\dfrac{5}{7}$

15. $3\dfrac{1}{7}$
$-\ 2\dfrac{4}{7}$

12-3 Subtracting, changing one denominator

Name_____

Change one fraction to match the other and then subtract.

1. $2\frac{3}{4}$
    $-1\frac{1}{2}$

2. $2\frac{5}{6}$
    $-1\frac{2}{3}$

3. $3\frac{2}{3}$
    $-2\frac{1}{6}$

4. $4\frac{4}{5}$
    $-2\frac{3}{10}$

5. $2\frac{2}{3}$
    $-1\frac{2}{6}$

6. $3\frac{7}{8}$
    $-2\frac{1}{4}$

7. $2\frac{4}{10}$
    $-1\frac{2}{5}$

8. $2\frac{2}{4}$
    $-1\frac{1}{2}$

9. $2\frac{4}{5}$
    $-1\frac{2}{10}$

10. $2\frac{2}{3}$
    $-1\frac{1}{6}$

11. $4\frac{5}{6}$
    $-2\frac{1}{3}$

12. $4\frac{4}{10}$
    $-3\frac{1}{5}$

13. $3\frac{7}{8}$
    $-1\frac{3}{4}$

14. $5\frac{6}{14}$
    $-2\frac{2}{7}$

15. $3\frac{3}{7}$
    $-2\frac{1}{14}$

12-4 Subtracting, changing both denominators

Name_____

First find the lowest common denominator. Next, subtract. Use scratch paper as needed if you want to draw models.

1. $2\dfrac{1}{2}$
   $-1\dfrac{1}{3}$

2. $2\dfrac{3}{4}$
   $-1\dfrac{2}{3}$

3. $3\dfrac{2}{3}$
   $-2\dfrac{1}{2}$

4. $2\dfrac{1}{2}$
   $-1\dfrac{1}{5}$

5. $2\dfrac{2}{3}$
   $-1\dfrac{2}{5}$

6. $3\dfrac{3}{5}$
   $-2\dfrac{1}{4}$

7. $3\dfrac{1}{2}$
   $-1\dfrac{2}{5}$

8. $2\dfrac{3}{4}$
   $-1\dfrac{1}{3}$

9. $2\dfrac{4}{5}$
   $-1\dfrac{2}{4}$

10. $2\dfrac{2}{3}$
    $-1\dfrac{1}{2}$

11. $4\dfrac{6}{7}$
    $-2\dfrac{1}{2}$

12. $4\dfrac{3}{4}$
    $-3\dfrac{1}{5}$

13. $3\dfrac{7}{8}$
    $-1\dfrac{1}{3}$

14. $4\dfrac{1}{3}$
    $-2\dfrac{1}{5}$

15. $2\dfrac{6}{7}$
    $-1\dfrac{1}{3}$

12-5 Subtracting, changing both denominators

Name_____

First find the lowest common denominator. Make improper fractions if needed, and then subtract.

1. $2\dfrac{1}{2}$
$-\quad\dfrac{2}{3}$

2. $1\dfrac{2}{3}$
$-\quad\dfrac{3}{4}$

3. $1\dfrac{1}{5}$
$-\quad\dfrac{1}{4}$

4. $2\dfrac{1}{7}$
$-1\dfrac{1}{2}$

5. $2\dfrac{1}{3}$
$-1\dfrac{1}{5}$

6. $2\dfrac{1}{2}$
$-1\dfrac{3}{5}$

7. $2\dfrac{1}{5}$
$-1\dfrac{1}{3}$

8. $2\dfrac{2}{3}$
$-1\dfrac{1}{2}$

9. $2\dfrac{1}{3}$
$-1\dfrac{1}{2}$

10. $2\dfrac{1}{4}$
$-1\dfrac{2}{3}$

11. $2\dfrac{1}{2}$
$-1\dfrac{1}{3}$

12. $2\dfrac{4}{5}$
$-1\dfrac{1}{2}$

13. $2\dfrac{3}{5}$
$-1\dfrac{1}{3}$

14. $2\dfrac{1}{2}$
$-1\dfrac{2}{9}$

15. $3\dfrac{1}{2}$
$-2\dfrac{4}{5}$

12-6 What I know about subtracting fractions

Name_____

Solve. Feel free to sketch models for yourself as you go.

1. $2\dfrac{3}{4}$
   $-\ 1\dfrac{2}{4}$
   _____

2. $2\dfrac{3}{6}$
   $-\ 1\dfrac{2}{6}$
   _____

3. $3\dfrac{2}{3}$
   $-\ 2\dfrac{1}{3}$
   _____

4. $6\dfrac{4}{10}$
   $-\ 3\dfrac{3}{10}$
   _____

5. $2\dfrac{1}{4}$
   $-\ 1\dfrac{3}{4}$
   _____

6. $2\dfrac{3}{8}$
   $-\ 1\dfrac{4}{8}$
   _____

7. $2\dfrac{1}{9}$
   $-\ 1\dfrac{2}{9}$
   _____

8. $2\dfrac{3}{6}$
   $-\ 2\dfrac{1}{6}$
   _____

9. $2\dfrac{4}{5}$
   $-\ 1\dfrac{2}{10}$
   _____

10. $2\dfrac{2}{3}$
    $-\ 1\dfrac{1}{6}$
    _____

11. $4\dfrac{5}{6}$
    $-\ 2\dfrac{1}{3}$
    _____

12. $4\dfrac{4}{10}$
    $-\ 3\dfrac{1}{5}$
    _____

13. $2\dfrac{4}{5}$
    $-\ 1\dfrac{2}{4}$
    _____

14. $2\dfrac{2}{3}$
    $-\ 1\dfrac{1}{2}$
    _____

15. $4\dfrac{6}{7}$
    $-\ 2\dfrac{1}{2}$
    _____

16. $4\dfrac{3}{4}$
    $-\ 3\dfrac{1}{5}$
    _____

17. $2\dfrac{1}{3}$
    $-\ 1\dfrac{2}{7}$
    _____

18. $2\dfrac{3}{4}$
    $-\ 1\dfrac{2}{3}$
    _____

19. $2\dfrac{1}{2}$
    $-\ 1\dfrac{4}{7}$
    _____

20. $2\dfrac{4}{5}$
    $-\ 1\dfrac{1}{2}$
    _____

MULTIPLYING FRACTIONS

Goals for This Chapter:

1. Reviewing the meaning of multiplication
2. Multiplication of whole numbers times fractions
3. Multiplying fractions
4. Cross simplifying of fractions
5. Multiplying mixed numbers

I. What does multiplication really mean?

Multiplication of fractions will be a whole lot easier if children understand and even visualize what is actually happening when we multiply. If they don't understand what multiplication means, they will resort to attempting to memorize procedures, and memorization is highly ineffective for many children.

Let's use a story, lots of examples, and hands-on activities!

One morning, Num and Nom's cousin, Avi Ator, dropped in just as the brothers were starting pizza baking for the day. Avi had broken her arm, so she didn't plan to help; she just wanted to watch.

Savory smells flooded the room when Num opened the door of the first oven. He slid a piping hot cheese pizza out of the oven and onto the counter in front of Nom before hurrying to pop another pizza into the oven.

Nom's job was to cut the fresh pizza into slices, wrap it, and slide it into a warming oven.

Five times Avi watched the brothers repeat this process. Num took a pizza to Nom, slid another one into the oven, and Nom cut and wrapped the pizza and put it into the warming oven. It was almost like a dance.

By the time Nom had cut and packaged the fifth pizza, this is what they had made:

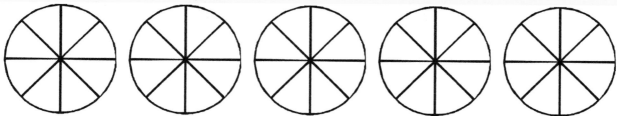

5 times Nom cut 8 slices of pizza. 5 x 8 = 40 pieces of pizza altogether.

This is what multiplication of whole numbers looks like.

II. A whole number times a fraction

But let's continue with our story.

Oh boy. All this pizza baking and cutting made Avi begin to drool. When Num noticed how hungry Avi looked, he grabbed a blue plate and slid a piping hot slice of pizza on it. That slice was 1/8 of a whole pizza.

Avi gulped down the pizza and looked longingly at the rest of the slices on the platter. Num served her another slice. Four times this happened!

Four times Num gave Avi 1/8 of the pizza. This is what it looks like:

4 times 1/8 = 4/8 of a whole pizza.

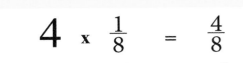

In the story about Avi and the pizza slices, we saw this:

$$4 \times \frac{1}{8} = \frac{4}{8}$$

times   1 slice   4 slices

Here's another example.

Avi's mother made extra large, yummy, chewy chocolate chip cookies. They were so large that she cut them into four pieces each. Avi brought 4 friends home with her. There were 5 children in all. All five children stared at the cookie plate.

So, Mom gave them each 1/4 of a cookie. Here is what that looked like:

$$5 \times \frac{1}{4} = \frac{5}{4}$$

times   1 piece   5 pieces

Out of 8/4 in all, the five children ate 5/4 or 1 1/4 of the cookies.

This is what multiplication of a whole number and a fraction looks like.

Let's practice a bit.

1. 2 x 1/3 = [2/3]

   a. Use a fraction strip for thirds. 2 x 1/3 is the same as saying, "Put an X on 1/3 two times."

   b. How many thirds did we mark? [2]

2. 2 x 2/5 = [4/5]

   a. Use the fifths fraction strip and X off 2/5 two times.

   b. How many fifths did we mark? [4]

3. 3 x 2/7 = [6/7]

   a. Use a sevenths fraction strip and X off 2/7 three times.

   b. How many sevenths did we mark? [6]

4. 2 x 3/10 = [6/10]

   a. Use the tenths fraction strip. X off 3/10 twice.

   b. How many tenths did we mark? [6]

The pattern we want the students to internalize is that Nom stays the same when we multiply a whole number times a fraction. It is only Num that changes. The "how many" is all we change. If we are speaking of thirds, for example, all that changes is how many 1/3 we have.

From models to symbols

Each time we multiplied a fraction by a whole number, we multiplied the Num by the whole number. Let's check and make sure this is correct.

1. 4 x 1/8 = 4/8 - Yes! Nom stayed the same!
So we could have written the problem like this:

$$4 \quad \times \quad \frac{1}{8} \quad \text{is the same as} \quad \frac{4 \times 1}{8}$$

2. 5 x 1/4 = 5/4
We could have written the problem like this:

$$5 \quad \times \quad \frac{1}{4} \quad \text{is the same as} \quad \frac{5 \times 1}{4}$$

3. 2 x 1/3 = 2/3
We could have written the problem like this:

$$2 \quad \times \quad \frac{1}{3} \quad \text{is the same as} \quad \frac{2 \times 1}{3}$$

4. 4 x 2/5 = 8/5
We could have written the problem like this:

$$4 \quad \times \quad \frac{2}{5} \quad \text{is the same as} \quad \frac{4 \times 2}{5}$$

5. 3 x 4/7 = 12/7
We could have written the problem like this:

$$3 \quad \times \quad \frac{4}{7} \quad \text{is the same as} \quad \frac{3 \times 4}{7}$$

Just pretend that Whole Number has to go upstairs to do business with Num. And to make it easier for Whole Number to talk with Num, we can make him a little stilt to stand on so they are the same height.

$$5 \quad \times \quad \frac{2}{5} \quad \text{is the same as} \quad \frac{5}{1} \quad \times \quad \frac{2}{5}$$

Rewrite these problems, putting the whole number up on a stilt:

1. 5 x 1/8   2. 5 x 1/4   3. 2 x 1/3   4. 4 x 2/5   5. 3 x 4/7

Hands On:
Use Resource 13-1. Multiplying whole numbers by fractions.

III. Multiply a fraction by another fraction

Let's do some hands-on model practice to start this section. This is going to be so much fun! Give the students Resource 13-2 to use along with their clockface models and strip models.

Have the students follow as you draw on the whiteboard and model for them what you want them to do.

1. **Say:** Find a model of halves.

    a. Say: The problem is 1/3 x 1/2. We can also say 1/3 **of** 1/2.

    b. Ask: What would you do to show 1/3 of 1/2?

[1/3 of 1/2 means you will divide Dom into **three** pieces with your pencil!]

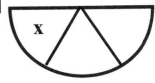

c. How many thirds of 1/2 do we need? Just one. So we can put an X on one of the thirds - or we can color it in.

d. Are those thirds really thirds of the whole? Nope! They are really sixths! So 1/3 x 1/2 = 1/6.

2. The problem is 1/2 x 1/2 or 1/2 of 1/2.

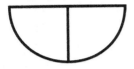

a. Ask: How would you mark or cut the model of 1/2 to show 1/2 x 1/2?

b. When the students have answered, point out that what changed was Nom. Nom got half as big as he was before.

What happened here is just the opposite of what happens when we do 2 x 1/2. In 2 x 1/2 we change Num and we end up with more than we started with.

The pattern we want the kids to internalize is that when we multiply a fraction by a fraction, Nom HAS to change. A fraction of something will always means breaking the piece into a smaller size. Example: 1/2 of a cookie is smaller than the whole. 1/3 of that 1/2 cookie is smaller yet! So NOM changes when we multiply fractions.

3. Say: The problem is 1/4 x 1/3.

a. Ask: Who is going to change in this operation? Num or Nom? [Nom] Let the students verbalize why this is so. [We will end up with only 1/4 of a 1/3 - Nom will get divided into small pieces.]

b. Say: We know Nom is the one changing in this problem because the fraction 1/4 has a number sitting on top of the 4 pushing him downstairs where Nom lives. That 4 tells us how many pieces to divide the 1/3 into. So here goes:

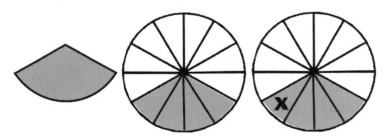

This illustration shows the 1/3 model in blue.

If you put the blue 1/3 over a 12ths model, you can see that the 1/3 was divided into fourths. Finally, you can see the X marking the 1/12 which is the answer to 1/4 x 1/3 (or 1/4 of 1/3).

Work through these problems together, asking the students to verbalize what to do at each step.

1. 1/5 x 1/3 [1/15]   2. 1/6 x 1/4 [1/24]   3. 1/2 x 1/5 [1/10]

4. 1/3 x 1/6 [1/18   5. 1/2 x 1/3 [1/6]   6. 1/3 x 1/7 [1/21]

Hands On:

Use Resource 13-3. Multiplying fractions by fractions.

The problem is 2/3 x 1/4. We know that Num will change to a 12 because that is the LCD of 3 and 4 and also because Nom in the 2/3 says to divide the 1/4 into 3 pieces. Let's grab our models for fourths and twelfths.

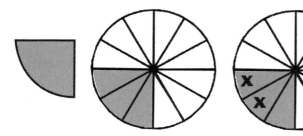

Look first at the model of 1/4. We are multiplying by 2/3. The three in the denominator tells us that we will be dividing 1/4 into three pieces. The two in the numerators tells us that we are going to keep 2 of those pieces. These are marked with an x.

The way to write out this problem and solve it without using models is this:

$$\frac{2}{3} \quad \text{x} \quad \frac{1}{4} \quad \text{is the same as} \quad \frac{2 \text{x} 1}{3 \text{x} 4} = \frac{2}{12}$$

Work the following problems together, asking students to direct your steps. Count answers correct whether or not they are simplified.

1. 2/5 x 1/2 [2/10 or 1/5]   2. 4/5 x 1/3 [4/15]   3. 2/5 x 1/4 [2/20 or 1/10]
4. 1/2 x 4/5 [4/10 or 2/5]   5. 2/3 x 1/2 [2/6 or 1/3]   6. 3/4 x 1/3 [3/12 or 1/4]

Hands On:
Use Resource 13-4. Multiplying fractions by fractions, part 2.

IV. Cross-simplifying when multiplying fractions

When I was young, one of the very few things I enjoyed about working with fractions was cross-simplifying before doing the required computation. Again, rather than just telling the students that they can cross-simplify, let's show them what it means.

The problem is: 3/4 x 4/5.

a. Use a 5ths strip.

b. Fold 1/5 under leaving 4/5 showing.

c. Now that we have 4/5, let's look at 3/4.

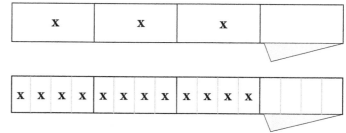

$$\frac{3}{4}$$

How many 5ths we need

How many pieces we cut 5ths into.

Let's divide each 5th into four pieces. How many fifths do we need? [3] The illustration above shows 3/4 of 4/5 marked with Xs and that equals12/20. [3 x 4 = 12 over 4 x 5 = 20]. But when we compare the fifths in the illustration we can plainly see that the answer we got (12/20) is exactly the same as 3/5. Look at the problem again.

$$\frac{3}{4} \times \frac{4}{5} \quad \text{is the same as} \quad \frac{3\times4}{4\times5} = \frac{12}{20} \quad \text{or} \quad \frac{3}{5}$$

If you look back at the original problem, do you see the answer there? Where is it?

$$\frac{3}{4} \times \frac{4}{5}$$

We can see that both Num and Nom are going to be multiplied by a 4, so why bother? Why not cross them out and omit that step? Crossing out the 4's will prevent us from having to multiply those big numbers! When we simplify a problem like this, we can only cross out numbers on a slant - one Nom and one Num - in an X shape.

Let's try a few other examples.

1. The problem is 2/3 x 3/4. And here is 3/4:

$$\frac{2}{3} \times \frac{3}{4}$$

Do you see anything we can simplify? [Yes. We can cross out the 3's - one Nom and one Num because they are on a slant.]

Now that we have crossed out the 3's 2/4 is left.

But 2/4 can be simplified as well because if you divide each number by 2, you will have 1/2 left over. And that is our answer! 1/2.

Let's do this same thing on the model so we can see clearly what we just did. Here is a model of 3/4:

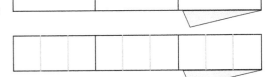

We will divide each 4th into 3 parts because that is Nom in the fraction 2/3.

Now we look at Num to see how many fractional parts we need. Num says two. So let's mark off two of the fourths.

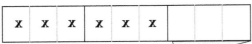

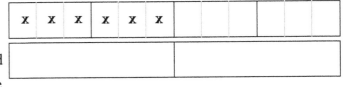

When we open our fourths model showing the selected parts, and we line it up to a model of halves, we can see that 2/3 x 3/4 is the same as 1/2.

2. The problem is 3/4 x 4/9.

    a. Have the students use a strip for 9ths and fold under 5 of the sections, letting just 4/9 show.

    b. Students will divide each 9th into four pieces or fourths.

    c. They will select 3 of the 9ths.

    d. Have them write the problem and multiply straight across. They should get 12/36. If you simplify that answer, you will have 1/3 because 12 is exactly a third of 36.

e. Now have them write the same problem again, but this time they will cross-simplify. They can cross out the fours and also simplify 3 and 9 by dividing both numbers by 3. The answer is 1/3.

f. Have them unfold their 9th strip and compare it to the 9ths strip. They should be able to see at a glance that 1/3 is the same as the selections they made on the 9ths strip.

3. The problem is 4/5 x 5/8

a. Use an 8ths fraction strip and fold under three sections so that 5 eighths show.

b. Divide each eighth into five pieces.

c. Select 4 of the eighths.

d. Multiply 4/5 x 5/8. The answer will be 20/40 or 1/2, once simplified.

e. Now have them write the problem again and this time cross-simplify. They can cross out the fives. Next they can divide both the 4 and the 8 by 4 and they will have 1/2 remaining.

f. Have them open their 8ths fraction strip and compare it to halves. Can they see that 4/5 of 5/8 is the same as 1/2?

Practice cross-simplifying these problems:

1. 2/5 x 5/8. Cross out the 5s and divide both the 2 and the 8 by 2. Answer is 1/4.

2. 3/7 x 7/8. Cross out the 7ths. You cannot divide 3 and 8 by the same number, so your answer is 3/8.

3. 1/2 x 2/5. Cross out the 2s and your answer is simply 1/5.

4. 3/5 x 5/6. Cross out the 5s. Divide both 3 and 6 by 3 and you will have 1/2.

Hands On:
Use Resource 13-5. Multiplying fractions using cross-simplification.

V. Multiplying mixed numbers

Multiplying mixed numbers can be daunting, but let's keep in mind that if we make improper fractions first, it is much easier.

1. The problem is 3 2/3 x 2 1/4.

If we don't make improper fractions and multiply straight across, we would have to do four multiplication problems and then simplify. We would multiply 3 x 2, then 3 x 1/4, then 2/3 x 2, and finally 2/3 x 1/4. Whew! I remember forgetting where I was when I multiplied mixed numbers using this method! Invariably I made mistakes!

a. So let's make improper fractions first. 3 2/3 becomes 3/3 + 3/3 + 3/3 + 2/3 = 11/3.

2 1/4 becomes 4/4 + 4/4+ 1/4 = 9/4.

b. Now let's multiply 11/3 x 9/4. Can we cross-simplify? YES!! Divide both 9 and 3 by 3.

Now our problem is 3/4 x 11 or 33/4. To get rid of the improper fraction, we can find that 4 goes into 33 8 times with 1/4 left over.

2. The problem is 1 2/3 x 2 1/2.

    a. Make improper fractions. 1 2/3 = 5/3 and 2 1/2 becomes 5/2.

    b. Can we cross-simplify? No.

    c. Multiply straight across. 5 x 5 = 25 and 3 x 2 = 6. The answer is 25/6.

    d. To simplify, divide 25 by 6 = 4 and you have 1/6 left over: 4 1/6.

3. The problem is 2 1/4 x 3 1/5.

    a. Make improper fractions. 9/4 x 16/5.

    b. You can cross-simplify. Divide the 4 and the 16 by 4. Now we have 9 x 4/5 or 36/5.

    c. Simplify 36/5 by dividing 36 by 5. 5 goes into 36 seven times with 1/5 left over, making 7 1/5.

4. The problem is 2 1/4 x 1 2/3.

    a. Make improper fractions. 2 1/4 becomes 9/4 and 1 2/3 becomes 5/3.

    b. Cross-simplify. Divide both 9 and 3 by 3. Now you have 3/4 x 5 = 15/4.

    c. To simplify, divide 15 by 4 and you end up with 3 3/4.

5. The problem is 2 1/5 x 2 1/2.

    a. Make improper fractions. 2 1/5 becomes 11/5 and 2 1/2 becomes 5/2.

    b. Cross-simplify. Delete both 5's and you have 11/2.

    c. To simplify, divide 11 by 2 and you end up with 5 1/2.

6. The problem is 1 1/6 x 2 2/3.

    a. Make improper fractions. 1 1/6 becomes 7/6 and 2 2/3 becomes 8/3.

    b. Cross-simplify. Divide 8 and 6 by 2. Now you have 7/3 x 4/3.

    c. Multiply straight across. Now we have 28/9.

    d. Simplify by dividing 28 by 9 and you get 3 1/9.

Hands On:
Use Resource 13-6. Multiplying mixed numbers.

If the students are comfortable with each section in this chapter, go ahead and use Resource 13-7 to assess their knowledge.

13-1 Multiplying fractions by whole numbers

Name_____

Put the whole number on stilts first if you are most comfortable with that. Then multiply across.

1. $2 \times \dfrac{3}{4} =$

2. $4 \times \dfrac{1}{5} =$

3. $2 \times \dfrac{1}{6} =$

4. $2 \times \dfrac{3}{5} =$

5. $2 \times \dfrac{5}{6} =$

6. $2 \times \dfrac{3}{10} =$

7. $3 \times \dfrac{1}{7} =$

8. $3 \times \dfrac{2}{3} =$

9. $2 \times \dfrac{1}{2} =$

10. $3 \times \dfrac{1}{7} =$

11. $4 \times \dfrac{3}{8} =$

12. $3 \times \dfrac{4}{5} =$

13. $4 \times \dfrac{1}{6} =$

14. $5 \times \dfrac{1}{2} =$

13-3 Multiplying fractions by fractions

Multiply across, Num times Num and Nom times Nom.

1. $\dfrac{1}{2}$ X $\dfrac{1}{3}$ =

2. $\dfrac{1}{4}$ X $\dfrac{1}{2}$ =

3. $\dfrac{1}{6}$ X $\dfrac{1}{3}$ =

4. $\dfrac{1}{2}$ X $\dfrac{1}{6}$ =

5. $\dfrac{1}{3}$ X $\dfrac{1}{3}$ =

6. $\dfrac{1}{2}$ X $\dfrac{1}{10}$ =

7. $\dfrac{1}{2}$ X $\dfrac{1}{2}$ =

8. $\dfrac{1}{3}$ X $\dfrac{1}{5}$ =

9. $\dfrac{1}{5}$ X $\dfrac{1}{2}$ =

10. $\dfrac{1}{4}$ X $\dfrac{1}{3}$ =

11. $\dfrac{1}{6}$ X $\dfrac{1}{4}$ =

12. $\dfrac{1}{2}$ X $\dfrac{1}{8}$ =

13. $\dfrac{1}{2}$ X $\dfrac{1}{7}$ =

14. $\dfrac{1}{3}$ X $\dfrac{1}{3}$ =

13-4 Multiplying fractions by fractions, part 2

Name_____

Multiply across, Num times Num and Nom times Nom.

1. $\dfrac{1}{4} \times \dfrac{2}{3} =$

2. $\dfrac{1}{3} \times \dfrac{2}{5} =$

3. $\dfrac{3}{4} \times \dfrac{1}{2} =$

4. $\dfrac{2}{3} \times \dfrac{1}{5} =$

5. $\dfrac{1}{2} \times \dfrac{7}{8} =$

6. $\dfrac{2}{3} \times \dfrac{2}{4} =$

7. $\dfrac{2}{5} \times \dfrac{2}{3} =$

8. $\dfrac{1}{6} \times \dfrac{2}{3} =$

9. $\dfrac{1}{2} \times \dfrac{2}{3} =$

10. $\dfrac{1}{6} \times \dfrac{2}{3} =$

11. $\dfrac{1}{5} \times \dfrac{2}{3} =$

12. $\dfrac{1}{3} \times \dfrac{4}{5} =$

13. $\dfrac{4}{5} \times \dfrac{1}{2} =$

14. $\dfrac{1}{2} \times \dfrac{5}{6} =$

13-5 Cross-simplifying fractions

Cross-simplify fractions and then multiply.

1. $\dfrac{2}{3}$ **x** $\dfrac{3}{4}$ =

2. $\dfrac{4}{5}$ **x** $\dfrac{5}{8}$ =

3. $\dfrac{2}{7}$ **x** $\dfrac{7}{8}$ =

4. $\dfrac{4}{5}$ **x** $\dfrac{1}{4}$ =

5. $\dfrac{9}{12}$ **x** $\dfrac{12}{18}$ =

6. $\dfrac{2}{5}$ **x** $\dfrac{1}{2}$ =

7. $\dfrac{7}{8}$ **x** $\dfrac{4}{5}$ =

8. $\dfrac{1}{5}$ **x** $\dfrac{5}{6}$ =

9. $\dfrac{3}{8}$ **x** $\dfrac{2}{3}$ =

10. $\dfrac{3}{5}$ **x** $\dfrac{5}{9}$ =

11. $\dfrac{5}{6}$ **x** $\dfrac{2}{5}$ =

12. $\dfrac{4}{7}$ **x** $\dfrac{3}{4}$ =

13. $\dfrac{5}{8}$ **x** $\dfrac{3}{5}$ =

14. $\dfrac{2}{3}$ **x** $\dfrac{9}{10}$ =

13-6 Multiplying mixed numbers

Turn mixed numbers into improper fractions, cross-simplify if possible, then multiply straight across.

1. $1 \frac{1}{2} \times 2 \frac{1}{3} =$

2. $2 \frac{1}{2} \times 1 \frac{1}{5} =$

3. $1 \frac{1}{8} \times 1 \frac{5}{6} =$

4. $2 \frac{1}{4} \times 2 \frac{1}{3} =$

5. $2 \frac{1}{3} \times 1 \frac{1}{4} =$

6. $2 \frac{1}{5} \times 1 \frac{2}{3} =$

7. $1 \frac{1}{4} \times 1 \frac{1}{2} =$

8. $1 \frac{1}{3} \times 2 \frac{1}{4} =$

9. $2 \frac{1}{3} \times 2 \frac{2}{5} =$

10. $1 \frac{1}{9} \times 1 \frac{1}{2} =$

11. $1 \frac{7}{8} \times 1 \frac{1}{3} =$

12. $1 \frac{4}{5} \times 1 \frac{1}{3} =$

13. $1 \frac{2}{3} \times 2 \frac{1}{4} =$

14. $1 \frac{2}{3} \times 1 \frac{2}{5} =$

1. $2 \times \dfrac{3}{4} =$

2. $\dfrac{1}{4} \times \dfrac{1}{2} =$

3. $\dfrac{3}{4} \times \dfrac{1}{2} =$

4. $\dfrac{4}{5} \times \dfrac{1}{4} =$

5. $\dfrac{9}{12} \times \dfrac{12}{18} =$

6. $2\dfrac{1}{5} \times 1\dfrac{2}{3} =$

7. $1\dfrac{1}{4} \times 1\dfrac{1}{2} =$

8. $3 \times \dfrac{2}{3} =$

9. $\dfrac{1}{5} \times \dfrac{1}{2} =$

10. $\dfrac{1}{6} \times \dfrac{2}{3} =$

11. $\dfrac{5}{6} \times \dfrac{2}{5} =$

12. $\dfrac{4}{7} \times \dfrac{3}{4} =$

13. $1\dfrac{2}{3} \times 2\dfrac{1}{4} =$

14. $1\dfrac{2}{3} \times 1\dfrac{2}{5} =$

14 DIVIDING FRACTIONS

Goals for This Chapter:

1. Dividing fractions by a whole number
2. Understanding why dividing is the same as "flip and multiply"
3. Dividing fractions by fractions
4. Dividing with mixed numbers

The idea of sharing equal parts is something familiar to children. If there are three friends eying a plate of 9 cookies, it would be natural for them to divide the cookies into 3 piles so each child can have a fair share. Basically, when we divide, we are starting with a whole and breaking it into smaller pieces in order to create equal shares. This is what happens each time Nom takes a whole pizza and divides it into eight slices.

I. Simple division of fractions by whole numbers

If we use models we will take the UGH out of dividing fractions. By this time, your students will know which type of model will help them the most. Let them choose what they want to use. In this section, we will be dividing fractions by a whole number when Num can be divided evenly by that number.

1. **Solve 3/4 ÷ 3**

   a. **Say:** Make a model for 3/4 and put an X in one space. 3/4 ÷ 3 = 1/4.

   b. **Ask:** Who changed in this problem? Num or Nom? [Num, because we could divide 3 by 3 to get 1. This also means we don't have to find LCD.]

   c. **Say:** Let's rewrite the problem to show that Whole Number was dealing with Num. We will build a stilt for Whole Number to stand on.

$$\frac{3}{4} \div 3 = \frac{1}{4} \text{ is the same as } \frac{3}{4} \div \frac{3}{1} = \frac{1}{4}$$

Critical thinking:

When we divide something by 3, is that the same as taking 1/3 of that same thing?

This illustration also shows 3/4 divided into thirds.

3/4 ÷ 3 means we had a 3/4 and cut it into three parts.

Is this the same as multiplying 3/4 by 1/3? [Yes. In both cases, the answer is 1/4]

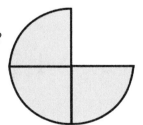

So is this statement correct?

$$\frac{3}{4} \div 3 = \frac{1}{4} \text{ is the same as } \frac{3}{4} \div \frac{3}{1} = \frac{1}{4} \text{ is the same as } \frac{3}{4} \times \frac{1}{3} = \frac{1}{4}$$

[Yes. In each case the answer is "One share is 1/4."]

Our goal is for the students to understand why flipping the second fraction and multiplying is the same as dividing.

2. **Solve 4/5 ÷ 2**

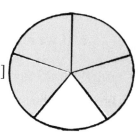

    a. **Say:** Make a model for 4/5 and divide by 2. $4/5 \div 2 = 2/5$

    b. **Say:** Rewrite the problem to show Whole Number on a stilt. [$4/5 \div 2/1 = 2/5$.]

    c. **Ask:** Who changed, Num or Nom? [Num. We divided 4 by 2.]

Critical thinking:

    Is dividing by two the same as multiplying by 1/2? Are these three problems really saying the same thing? [Yes. Say Avi sees Num with an apple and she wants to share it. If she says, "Could you divide that apple by two so I can have some?" is that not the same as her asking, "Could I have 1/2 of your apple?"]

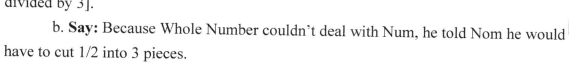

$$\frac{4}{5} \div 2 = \frac{2}{5} \qquad \frac{4}{5} \div \frac{2}{1} = \frac{2}{5} \qquad \overset{2}{\frac{4}{5}} \times \underset{1}{\frac{1}{2}} = \frac{2}{5}$$

    So if "÷ 2" is the same thing as "x 1/2", all we need to do is flip the second fraction on its head and multiply straight across after we have cross-simplified.

Hands On:

    Use Resource 14-1. Simple division of fractions by whole numbers. Work the first couple together as needed by the students.

II. Dividing fractions by whole numbers, changing Nom

1. **Solve 1/2 ÷ 3**

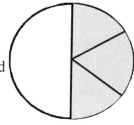

    a. **Ask:** Can you divide Num by 3? [No. Num is only a 1 and it cannot be divided by 3].

    b. **Say:** Because Whole Number couldn't deal with Num, he told Nom he would have to cut 1/2 into 3 pieces.

    c. When this happened, 1/2 turned into three sixths, and each of the 3 shares is just 1/6 of the whole. So $1/2 \div 3 = 1/6$.

Critical thinking:

    Is saying 1/2 ÷ 3 the same as saying 3/6 ÷ 3? [Yes. Changing 1/2 to 3/6 just makes it easier to divide.]

    Is saying 1/2 ÷ 3 the same as saying 1/3 of 1/2? [Yes. 1/3 of 1/2 = 1/6.] If this is the case, are these three problems all saying the same thing? [Yes!]

$$\frac{1}{2} \div 3 = \frac{1}{6} \qquad \frac{3}{6} \div \frac{3}{1} = \frac{1}{6} \qquad \frac{1}{2} \times \frac{1}{3} = \frac{1}{6}$$

2. **Solve 3/4 ÷ 4**

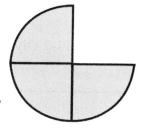 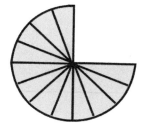

    a. **Ask:** Can you divide Num by 4? [No because Num is only a 3 and it cannot be divided by 4].

    b. **Say:** Because Whole Number couldn't deal with Num,

he went downstairs to tell Nom he would have to cut 3/4 into 4 pieces each.

      c. If we multiply 3/4 by 4 it changes to 12/16 Now we can divide 12/16 by 4. Each share is 3/16.

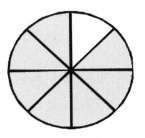

Critical thinking:

    Is 3/4 ÷ 4 the same as asking "What is 1/4 of 3/4?" [Yes]

    So 3/4 ÷ 4 is the same as 3/4 x 1/4. Both are 3/16.

3. Solve 7/8 ÷ 2

      a. **Ask:** Can we divide Nom by 2? [No. 7 can't be divided by 2].

      b. **Say:** Because Whole Number couldn't divide Num, he went downstairs and told Nom he would have to cut 7/8 into 2 pieces each.

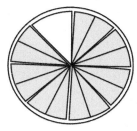

      c. **Say:** Cutting the pieces is just like multiplying 7/8 by 2. We will turn 7/8 into 14/16 which can be divided by 2. Each share is 7/16.

Critical thinking:

    Is 7/8 ÷ 2 the same as asking "What is 1/2 of 7/8?" [Yes]

      So 7/8 ÷ 2 is the same as 7/8 x 1/2. Both are 7/16.

      You can see from the model that while Nom got cut in half, doubling the number from 8 to 16, when you take half of the model, Num is still 7.

      Explore other fractions divided by 2 and see if you can find the pattern:

      Use: 1/3 ÷ 2   3/5 ÷ 2   5/8 ÷ 2   1/8 ÷ 2   1/7 ÷ 2   3/7 ÷ 2

     In each of these problems, you cannot divide Num by Whole Number, so you cut Nom in half. The pattern is that when you divide a fraction by 2, Num stays the same while Nom doubles (because he is cut in half). When dividing by 2, 1/3 becomes 1/6, 3/5 becomes 3/10, 5/8 becomes 5/16, etc.

Continue to work through the following problems:

    1. **1/5 ÷ 2**   1/5 cut into two pieces = 1/10   or   1/5 x 1/2 = 1/10.

    2. **2/3 ÷ 4**   Will have to cut thirds into 4 pieces.   8/12 ÷ 4 = 4/12 or 1/3 or 1/4 of 2/3.

      Cross simplify and multiply: 1/2 x 1/3 = 1/6.

    3. **5/6 ÷ 2**   Half of 5/6 = 5/12. We have to cut Nom in half because you cannot divide 5 by 2.

      Or, flip and multiply: 5/6 x 1/2 = 5/12.

    4. **4/5 ÷ 3**   Cut 5ths into 3 parts each making 15ths. 12/15 ÷ 3 = 4/15   Or, flip, cross-simplify, and multiply: 12/15 x 1/3 turns into 4/15 x 1 = 4/15.

Hands On:
    Use Resource 14-2 Dividing fractions by whole numbers, changing Nom.

III. Dividing fractions by fractions

Having learned about the flip and multiply trick, it might be tempting to skip the hands-on work in order to save time. But let's not skip that important tactile work. We want our students to understand what is going on when we divide a fraction by a fraction. Something weird and wonderful happens! It's like the Pinocchio Effect. Our current number sense dictates that when you divide something, you end up with smaller portions, right? 1 ÷ 2 = 1/2. Smaller. If you divide a whole cookie into three pieces, the three pieces are much smaller than the whole. Smaller.

But when we divide by fractions instead of whole numbers, the Pinocchio Effect comes into play. Bigger.

For example, when we say, "Solve 1 ÷ 1/2" what we are really saying is "How many 1/2 are in a whole?" And of course we know there are 2 halves in a whole. So, 1 ÷ 1/2 = 2. Bigger. The Pinocchio Effect!

Solve with models:

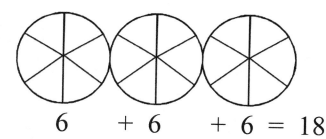

$$6 \quad + \quad 6 \quad + \quad 6 = 18$$

3 ÷ 1/6 means "How many 1/6 are in 3? We can solve this first by writing 3/1 ÷ 1/6 or 3/1 x 6 = 18. There are six 1/6 in one whole, of course, so there would be 18 sixths in 3 wholes.

If you rewrite this problem, it becomes simple: 3/1 ÷ 1/6 is the same as 3/1 x 6/1 or 18.

1. Solve 1/2 ÷ 1/3

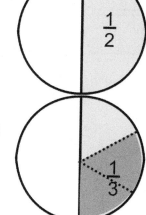

a. Build a model for 1/2.

b. The question is, "How many 1/3 are there in 1/2?" If we were to guess, we would know that there is at least one 1/3 in 1/2 because 1/3 is smaller than 1/2.

c. Lay a 1/3 model over a 1/2 model. We can see that there is 1 1/2 thirds that fit into 1/2. (The blue represents the 1/2 while the green represents 1/3).

d. Let's check our work by flipping and multiplying: 1/2 x 3 = 1 1/2. It works!

2. Solve 3/4 ÷ 1/3

a. Build a model for 3/4.

b. The question is, "How many 1/3 are there in 3/4?" If we were to guess, we would know that there is at least one 1/3 in 1/2 because 1/3 is smaller than 3/4.

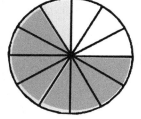

c. Lay a 1/3 model over the 3/4 model. Oh, there's room for another 1/3. Add the second 1/3 model over the 3/4 model. We can see that there are 2 1/4 thirds in 3/4.

d. Let's check our work by flipping and multiplying. 3/4 x 3 = 9/4 or 2 1/4.

3. Solve 5/3 ÷ 1/4

a. Build a model for 5/3 (see the blue strip). How many 1/4 can you fit into 5/3? (see the green strip).

				$\frac{5}{3}$	

				6 fourths	$\frac{2}{3}$	

b. Let's flip and multiply to check our work: 5/3 x 4/1 = 20/3 or 6 2/3. It works!

4. **Solve 7/12 ÷ 1/4**

   a. Build a model for 7/12. How many 1/4 can you fit into 7/12? [2 1/3].

1	2	$\frac{1}{3}$		

b. Let's flip and multiply to check our work: 7/12 x 4/1 and if we cross-simplify we have 7/3 x 1 = 7/3 or 2 1/3. Once again, it works!

5. **Solve 5/6 ÷ 1/3**

   a. Build a model for 5/6. How many 1/3 can you fit into 5/6? [2 1/2].

			$\frac{5}{6}$	

1	2	$\frac{1}{2}$	

b. Let's flip and multiply to check our work: 5/6 x 3/1 and if we cross-simplify we have 5/2 x 1 = 5/2 or 2 1/2. Once again, it works!

6. **Solve 7/8 ÷ 1/2**

   a. Build a model for 7/8. How many 1/3 can you fit into 5/6? [1 3/4].

					$\frac{7}{8}$	

1				$\frac{3}{4}$	

b. Let's flip and multiply to check our work: 7/8 x 2/1 and if we cross-simplify we have 7/4 x 1 = 7/4 or 1 3/4. Once again, it works!

Hands On:
Use Resource 14-3. Dividing fractions by fractions.

IV. Dividing with mixed numbers

This section will bring dividing fractions into real life situations. Let's use stories and models both for this exercise.

1. **Story:** Avi had 2 1/4 hours in which to do three chores. How much time will she have for each chore?

   a. Write a **problem** for the story: 2 1/4 hours divided by 3 chores or 2 1/4 ÷ 3. Or better yet, 9/4 ÷ 3.

   Can Whole Number divide Num now? [Yes. 9 ÷ 3 = 3. Each chore took 3/4 hour].

   b. Let's use **models** to show the problem:

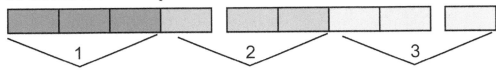

Here we have two wholes and 1/4 divided equally between 3 chores. 3/4 of an hour for each chore.

c. Now let's try our lovely shortcut and see if we get the same result.

The problem is 2 1/4 ÷ 3.

Change the mixed number to an improper fraction: 9/4 ÷ 3

Put Whole Number on a stilt as he is dealing with Num: 9/4 ÷ 3/1.

Now flip the second fraction: 9/4 x 1/3.

Cross simplify: 3/4 x 1/1 = 3/4. Yes! Same answer!

2. **Story:** The Ator brothers had 2 1/2 pizzas to split with 5 people.

a. Let's write a **problem** for the story: 2 1/2 ÷ 5 or 5/2 ÷ 5. Whole Number can deal with Num, so the problem is super easy! 5/2 ÷ 5/1 is simply 1/2. Each person gets 1/2 of a pizza!

b. We can flip and multiply to check our work: 5/2 ÷ 5 is like saying 5/2 x 1/5. Cross-simplify and you have 1/2.

3. **Story:** The Ator brothers had 2 1/2 pizzas. How many 1/8 slices can they get out of that much pizza?

a. Let's write a **problem** for the story: 2 1/2 pizzas divided by 1/8. Or 5/2 ÷ 1/8. How many 1/8 are in 5/2? Can Whole Number deal with Num? [No. He has a 1 pushing him downstairs to deal with Nom. He tells Nom to cut each whole into 8 pieces].

b. If we multiply 5/2 x 8 to get a new LCD, that is our answer. There are 20 8ths in 2 1/5.

c. Let's use **models** to show the problem:

Here we have 2 wholes and 1/2 divided equally by 1/8. How many 1/8 do we have in all?

8 + 8 + 4 = 20/8.

c. Now let's try flip and multiply. The problem is 5/2 x 8/1. 5x 8 = 40/2 or 20. If we flip, cross-simplify and then multiply we have: 5/2 x 8/1 = 5/1 x 4/1 = 20.

Compare Story 2 and Story 3. When dividing by Whole Number, the answer gets smaller, but when dividing by a fraction, the answer is larger because the Pinocchio Effect takes over!

4. **Story:** Num went to the market to get tomatoes for pizza sauce. He paid $2.50 for 3 1/3 pounds of tomatoes. How much did each pound cost?

a. Write a problem for the story: 2 1/2 dollars ÷ 3 1/3 pounds of tomatoes. Or 5/2 ÷ 10/3. In order to divide, we have to have the same denominator and the LCD is 6. Our problems now is 15/6 ÷ 20/6. Ugh. This is bringing back all the times I disliked fractions intensely when I was a kid! What this problem really is asking now is "What part of 20 is 15?" 15 = 3/4 of 20. But let's do this a more friendly way.

b. Let's use **models** to show the problem: Here we see 3 full pounds and 1/3 pound of tomatoes.

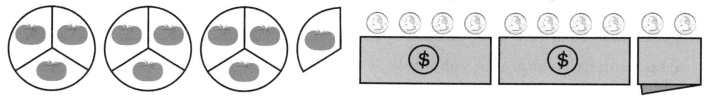

We also see $2.50. I noticed when I was solving this problem with models that 3 1/3 pounds of tomatoes

were really 10 /3 of tomatoes. I noticed also that it is easy to divide $2.50 into 10 parts to match the ten 3rds in the model. If we were to lay a quarter on top of each 1/3, we would see that the cost of 1 pound of tomatoes is 3 quarters or 3/4. That is our answer: The cost per pound of tomatoes is 3/4 of a dollar.

c. Now let's flip and multiply to solve the problem! 5/2 ÷ 10/3 is the same as saying 5/2 x 3/10. We can cross-simplify and arrive at 1/2 x 3/2 or 3/4 of a dollar. Which is the easiest way to solve this problem?

5. **Story:** Nom paid $2.25 for 3/4 of a pound of chocolate. If 3/4 of a pound cost $2.25, what would a whole pound cost?

a. Write a **problem** for the story: 2 1/4 dollars ÷ 3/4 pounds of candy or 9/4 ÷ 3/4. Because Noms are the same and 9 can easily be divided by 3, we can get our answer pretty easily. 3 is our answer.

b. Let's show the problem in a **model**. Here is 3/4 pound of candy and also the $2.25:

Ask the students how they would approach this problem? Would they pile quarters on each of the three quarters of the pound? If so, how many quarters would go in each quarter of a pound? [3 because there are 9 quarters and three 4ths to split them between. Now, back to the original question: If 3/4 of a pound of chocolate costs $2.25, how much will a whole pound cost? [If we put the same number of quarters in the blank space, how many quarters would we have in all? 12 quarters or $3.00].

c. Now let's flip and multiply! 9/4 x 4/3. Simplify and you have 3/1 or $3.00.

6. **Story:** The Ator brothers were about to close for the night when all of a sudden someone banged on the door. There was a hysterical boy at the door yelling, "I have to get some pizza!"

Nom hurried to the warming oven and peeked in. "I have 2/3 of a pizza left. I will give it to you for $9.33." "Oh thank you!" yelled the boy and plunked down his money. Then the boy asked, "If 2/3 of a pizza costs 9 1/3 dollars, how much would a whole pizza cost?"

"That's for you to figure out, Son," said Nom. When the boy got home, he drew out the problem. Here is a picture of 9 1/3 dollars divided by 2/3. How many 2/3 are there in all? [14].

a. Let's write the **problem** along with him. $9.33 is divided by 2/3 or 9 1/3 ÷ 2/3 or 28/3 ÷ 2/3.

(Remember we are dividing by a fraction, so the Pinocchio Effect will take over and our answer will be larger than before.)

The boy divided his dollars in thirds first - one third for each 1/3 of the pizza. He found that each third of a pizza cost 14/3 of a dollar. All he had to do was figure out what all three thirds would cost. He multiplied 14 x 3 and found it was 42/3. If he divided 42 by 3, the answer is 14. One whole pizza cost $14.00.

b. Would it not be simpler to flip and multiply? Let's try it. 28/3 ÷ 2/3 is the same as 28/3 x 3/2. When we cross-simplify, we have 14/1 or just plain 14.

7. **Solve:** 1 3/4 ÷ 7/8.

a. What the problem is asking is, "How many 7/8 are in 1 3/4?" Rewrite the problem first. 7/4 ÷ 7/8. Or even better, multiply the whole fraction by 2 so we can divide Num. 14/8 ÷ 7/8. How many 7s in 14? [2].

b. Let's flip and multiply now and compare our answer: 7/4 x 8/7 becomes 2/1 or 2.

Hands On:
Use Resource 14-4. Dividing fractions and mixed numbers.

V. Review key ideas about dividing fractions

1. When you divide fractions by whole numbers, the pieces get smaller and smaller.

For example: 1/2 ÷ 3 means take a half and divide it into three pieces.

2. When you divide anything by a fraction, the Pinocchio Effect takes over and your answer will be larger than what you started with.

For example: 3 ÷ 1/2 means "How many 1/2 are in 3?" If you cut each whole into halves, how many halves would you have? [6].

For example: 1/2 ÷ 1/3 means "How many 1/3 fit inside 1/2?" Obviously more than 1. Our answer is 1 1/2.

3. Mixed numbers divided by fractions makes the Pinocchio Effect kick in again!

For example: 3 1/2 ÷ 1/6 means "How many 1/6 are in 3 1/2. If each whole has 6 sixths, we will have 18 sixths in the wholes and 3 more in the half. So 3 1/2 ÷ 1/6 = 21.

Hands On:
Use Resource 14-5. Dividing mixed numbers by mixed numbers.

Critical thinking:

What are some strategies we have learned we can use when dividing?

1. Use models or draw pictures.

2. Find LCD when needed.

3. Flip and multiply.

Ask the students to share their own thoughts about how their minds work when they are solving division problems.

Hands On:
Use Resource 14-6 for assessment when you feel your students are ready.

14-1 Dividing fractions by whole numbers

Name_____

Put the whole number on stilts first if you are most comfortable with that. Then divide across. #1 is done for you.

1. $\dfrac{3}{4} \div \dfrac{3}{1} = \dfrac{1}{4}$

2. $\dfrac{2}{3} \div 2 =$

3. $\dfrac{4}{7} \div 2 =$

4. $\dfrac{5}{8} \div 5 =$

5. $\dfrac{4}{7} \div 4 =$

6. $\dfrac{9}{10} \div 3 =$

7. $\dfrac{3}{4} \div 3 =$

8. $\dfrac{4}{5} \div 2 =$

9. $\dfrac{4}{5} \div 4 =$

10. $\dfrac{4}{9} \div 4 =$

11. $\dfrac{6}{7} \div 2 =$

12. $\dfrac{6}{7} \div 3 =$

13. $\dfrac{3}{10} \div 3 =$

14. $\dfrac{4}{5} \div 2 =$

14-2 Dividing fractions by whole numbers

For each problem, make whole number a fraction, flip, cross-simplify, and multiply. #1 is done for you.

1. $\dfrac{6}{7} \div \dfrac{3}{1}$ $\quad$ $\dfrac{\cancel{6}^{2}}{7} \times \dfrac{1}{\cancel{3}_{1}} = \dfrac{2}{7}$

8. $\dfrac{4}{5} \div 2 =$

2. $\dfrac{2}{3} \div 2 =$

9. $\dfrac{3}{5} \div 3 =$

3. $\dfrac{2}{3} \div 4 =$

10. $\dfrac{4}{9} \div 2 =$

4. $\dfrac{2}{9} \div 2 =$

11. $\dfrac{5}{7} \div 5 =$

5. $\dfrac{2}{5} \div 2 =$

12. $\dfrac{6}{7} \div 2 =$

6. $\dfrac{2}{7} \div 2 =$

13. $\dfrac{3}{10} \div 3 =$

7. $\dfrac{3}{4} \div 3 =$

14. $\dfrac{4}{5} \div 2 =$

14-3 Dividing fractions by fractions

Divide these fractions. 1. flip the second fraction 2. cross-simplify 3. multiply. The first is done for you.

1. $\dfrac{3}{4} \div \dfrac{1}{2}$ $\qquad$ $\dfrac{3}{\underset{2}{\cancel{4}}} \times \dfrac{\overset{1}{\cancel{2}}}{1} = \mathbf{1}\dfrac{1}{2}$

8. $\dfrac{4}{5} \div \dfrac{1}{5} =$

2. $\dfrac{2}{3} \div \dfrac{1}{3} =$

9. $\dfrac{3}{4} \div \dfrac{3}{5} =$

3. $\dfrac{2}{3} \div \dfrac{1}{6} =$

10. $\dfrac{4}{5} \div \dfrac{3}{4} =$

4. $\dfrac{1}{3} \div \dfrac{1}{9} =$

11. $\dfrac{1}{2} \div \dfrac{1}{6} =$

5. $\dfrac{2}{3} \div \dfrac{1}{12} =$

12. $\dfrac{3}{4} \div \dfrac{1}{6} =$

6. $\dfrac{5}{6} \div \dfrac{1}{2} =$

13. $\dfrac{5}{8} \div \dfrac{1}{2} =$

7. $\dfrac{2}{3} \div \dfrac{2}{5} =$

14. $\dfrac{3}{5} \div \dfrac{3}{8} =$

14-4 Dividing fractions and mixed numbers

Name_____

Turn mixed numbers into improper fractions, flip the second fraction, cross-simplify if possible, then multiply straight across.

1. $1\frac{1}{2} \div \frac{1}{4}$ $\frac{3}{2} \times \frac{4}{1}^{2} = 6$

8. $1\frac{2}{3} \div \frac{1}{6} =$

2. $2\frac{1}{2} \div \frac{1}{2} =$

9. $2\frac{2}{5} \div \frac{1}{5} =$

3. $1\frac{3}{8} \div \frac{1}{4} =$

10. $1\frac{2}{3} \div \frac{1}{3} =$

4. $1\frac{2}{3} \div \frac{1}{2} =$

11. $1\frac{1}{4} \div \frac{5}{6} =$

5. $2\frac{1}{3} \div \frac{2}{6} =$

12. $1\frac{1}{4} \div \frac{1}{2} =$

6. $2\frac{1}{4} \div \frac{1}{6} =$

13. $1\frac{2}{5} \div \frac{4}{5} =$

7. $2\frac{1}{6} \div \frac{2}{3} =$

14. $1\frac{1}{6} \div \frac{3}{4} =$

14-5 Dividing mixed numbers by mixed numbers

Name_____

Turn mixed numbers into improper fractions, flip the second fraction, cross-simplify if possible, then multiply straight across.

1. $2\frac{1}{2} \div 1\frac{2}{3}$ $\frac{5}{2} \times \frac{3}{5} = \frac{3}{2} = 1\frac{1}{2}$

8. $2\frac{1}{4} \div 1\frac{3}{4} =$

2. $2\frac{1}{2} \div 1\frac{1}{4} =$

9. $2\frac{1}{2} \div 1\frac{1}{6} =$

3. $2\frac{1}{3} \div 1\frac{2}{3} =$

10. $1\frac{3}{4} \div 1\frac{1}{4} =$

4. $2\frac{2}{3} \div 1\frac{1}{3} =$

11. $1\frac{1}{6} \div 1\frac{1}{3} =$

5. $3\frac{1}{2} \div 1\frac{3}{4} =$

12. $3\frac{1}{3} \div 1\frac{1}{6} =$

6. $2\frac{5}{6} \div 1\frac{1}{3} =$

13. $1\frac{7}{8} \div 1\frac{1}{4} =$

7. $4\frac{1}{2} \div 2\frac{1}{4} =$

14. $3\frac{1}{3} \div 1\frac{1}{6} =$

14-6 What I know about dividing fractions

Name_____

You are so awesome! Look at all you have learned about fractions!

1. $\dfrac{2}{3} \div 2 =$

2. $\dfrac{2}{3} \div 3 =$

3. $\dfrac{2}{3} \div \dfrac{1}{4} =$

4. $\dfrac{1}{3} \div \dfrac{1}{6} =$

5. $1\dfrac{2}{3} \div \dfrac{1}{2} =$

6. $2\dfrac{1}{3} \div \dfrac{2}{6} =$

7. $1\dfrac{7}{8} \div 1\dfrac{1}{4} =$

8. $\dfrac{4}{5} \div 4 =$

9. $\dfrac{3}{5} \div 2 =$

10. $\dfrac{4}{7} \div \dfrac{1}{2} =$

11. $\dfrac{1}{2} \div \dfrac{1}{5} =$

12. $1\dfrac{1}{4} \div \dfrac{5}{6} =$

13. $1\dfrac{1}{4} \div \dfrac{1}{2} =$

14. $2\dfrac{1}{3} \div 1\dfrac{2}{3} =$

ANSWER KEYS

The large number is the page number of the Resource.

The number with a dash is the Resource number.

Answers are numbered as on the Resource sheet.

Page	Resource	

Page	Resource	
14	1-1	1. Area
		2. Length
		3. Set
		4. Set
		5. Set
		6. Length
		7. Area
		8. Length
		9. Area
		10. Length
		11. Area
		12. Set
15	1-2	1. X
		2. OK
		3. X
		4. X
		5. X
		6. X
		7. OK
		8. OK
		9. X
		10. OK
16	1-3	1. 3 cars each
		2. 2 crackers each
		3. 4 figures each
		4. half an apple
		5. cut into 10 pieces
		6. 2 each
17	1-4	1. Set
		2. Length
		3. Area
		4. X
		5. X
		6. O
		7. O
		8. X
		9. 4 pieces
		10. 8 pieces
		11. 2 each
		12. 2 each
		13. a whole broken into pieces

Page	Resource	
22	2-2	One-Whole
		Two-Halves
		Three-Thirds
		Four-Fourths
		Five-Fifths
		Six-Sixths
		Seven-Sevenths
		Eight-Eighths
		Nine-Ninths
		Ten-Tenths
		1. Eighths
		2. Thirds
		3. Fourths
		4. Sevenths
		5. Sixths
		6. Fifths
		7. Halves
23	2-3 A	1. Fourths
		2. Halves
		3. Sixths
		4. Sevenths
		5. Twelfths
		6. Eighths
		7. Fourths
		8. Fifths
24	2-3 B	1. Eighths
		2. Ninths
		3. Thirds
		4. Sixths
		5. Fourths
		6. Fifths
		7. Sevenths
		8. Thirds
25	2-4 A	Answers will vary.
26	2-4 B	Answers will vary.
27	2-4 C	Answers will vary.
28	2-5	Answers will vary.

Page	Resource	
29	2-6	1. Whole
		Halves
		Thirds
		Fourths
		Fifths
		Sixths
		Sevenths
		Eighths
		2. Twelfths
		3. Thirds
		4. Sixths
		5. Eighths
		6. Eighths
		7. Fifths
		8. Sevenths
		9. Fourths
		10. Sixths
37	3-1	1. Denominator
		2. To name
		3. Numerator
		4. To count
		5. Num
		6. Nom
		7. "One who"
		8. 1/3
		1/4
		1/5
		1/6
38	3-2	one $\frac{1}{2}$ half
		two $\frac{2}{3}$ thirds
		one $\frac{1}{4}$ fourth
		four $\frac{4}{5}$ fifths
		two $\frac{2}{6}$ sixths
		three $\frac{3}{7}$ sevenths
		five $\frac{5}{8}$ eighths

Page	Resource		Page	Resource		Page	Resource	
39	3-3	1. 2/6 2. 2/7 3. 4/11 4. 5/12 5. 2/7 6. 1/6 7. 3/9 8. 1/7 9. 1/4 10. 3/5	50	4-3	1. 6/4 2. 6/7 3. 7/4 4. 2/6 5. 2/6 6. 3/7 7. 5/12 8. 5/7	62	5-5	1. Color 5 boxes 2. Color 7 boxes 3. Color 8 boxes 4. Color 11 boxes 5. Color 12 boxes
40	3-4	Colored except 3 3/8 Cut into 6 pieces 3/6	52	4-5	1. 1/5 2. 1/3 3. 2/3 4. 2/7 5. 3/8 6. 2/5 7. 2/4 8. 1/3 9. 1/11 10. 2/8 11. 10/11 12. 2/10 13. 1/9 14. 3/5	63	5-6	1. Color 13 boxes, 13/7 2. Color 11 boxes, 11/6 3. Color 6 boxes, 6/4 4. Color 10 boxes, 10/8 5. Color 9 boxes, 9/5
41	3-5	1. 3/5 2. 5/8 3. 2/5 4. 7/12 5. 4/10 6. 25/100 7. 3/13 8. 1/4 9. 3/8 10. 5/12				64	5-7	1. 3/3 + 1/3 = 4/3 2. 5/5 + 3/5 = 8/5 3. 6/6 + 5/6 = 11/6 4. 11/11 + 8/11 = 19/11 5. Color 17 spaces 6. Color 9 spaces 7. Color 6 spaces 8. Color 5 spaces
			58	5-1	1. 24/8 2. 9/8 3. 5/3 4. 5/4 5. 9/6 6. 11/9	65	5-7	Circle 10, 11, 12, 15, 16, 17 Circle 20, 22, 23, 26
42	3-6	1. Denominator names 2. Numerator counts 3. 1/4 4. 5/12 5. 3/7 6. Color 6 boxes 7. Color 2 boxes 8. Color 4 boxes 9. 3/9 10. 7/10 11. Answer varies	60	5-3	1. Eighths, 10, 10/8 2. Halves, 5, 5/2 3. Fifths, 7, 7/5 4. Tenths, 16, 16/10 5. Sevenths, 11, 11/7	75	6-3	1. 1 4/8 2. 1 5/7 3. 1 5/6 4. 1 3/5 5. 1 1/4
			61	5-4	1. Eighths, 8, 8/8, 2/8 2. Halves, 2, 2/2, 1/2 3. Fifths, 5, 5/5, 2/5 4. Tenths, 10, 10/10, 6/10 5. Sevenths, 7, 7/7, 4/7	76	6-4	1. 1 2/5 2. 1 1/6 3. 1 3/4 4. 2 2/3 5. 1 2/7 6. 1 5/8 7. 1 1/2 8. 1 4/11 9. 1 3/10 10. 1 4/5 11. 1 1/4 12. 1 3/6 13. 1 1/8 14. 1 5/7 15. 1 7/9 16. 2 1/2

Page	Resource		Page	Resource		Page	Resource	
77	6-5	1. 7/5	87	7-1	1. 1/4	92	7-6	1. Color 4, 1 1/4
		2. 7/6			2. 1/3			2. Color 3, 1 2/3
		3. 7/4			3. 3/4			3. Color 2, 2 1/2
		4. 7/3			4. 5/6			4. Color 6, 1 2/6
		5. 12/7			5. 2/3			5. Color 4, 1 1/4
		6. 11/8			6. 1/6			6. Color 2, 1 1/2
		7. 5/2			7. 7/8			7. Color 5, 1 4/5
		8. 14/11			8. 2/8			8. Color 6, 1 3/6
		9. 14/10						
		10. 14/5	88	7-2	1. Color 2	93	7-7	1. Draw 8 dots
		11. 9/4			2. Color 3			2. Draw 2 triangles
		12. 8/6			3. Color 4			3. 1/4
		13. 13/8			4. Color 5			4. Draw 12 dots
		14. 9/7			5. Color 1			5. 1/5
		15. 13/9			6. Color 4			6. Draw 2 dots
		16. 8/3			7. Color 7			7. Draw 5 hexagons
					8. Color 5			8. Draw 5 dots
78	6-6	Part 1						
		1-3 Answers will vary.	89	7-3	1. 1 whole 4 dots more	95	7-9	1. 2/8 or 1/4
					2. 1 whole 7 loose			2. 1/4
		Part 2			3. 1 whole 3 more			3. 3/6 or 1/2
		1. 1 8/11			4. 1 whole 3 more			4. Color 3 dots
		2. 1 5/6			5. 1 whole 4 more			5. Color 5 pieces
		3. 1 2/4			6. 1 whole 1 more			6. Color 3 parts
		4. 1 3/4			7. 2 wholes 3 dots more			
		5. 1 3/5			8. 1 whole 3 more	96	7-9	1. Draw 1 whole + 4
		6. 1 1/3						2. Draw 2 wholes + 1
		7. 1 2/9	90	7-4	1. Draw 3 circles			3. Draw 1 whole + 2
		8. 1 4/8			2. Draw 4 triangles			4. Draw 4 triangles
					3. Draw 6 squares			5. Draw 6 squares
79	6-6	Part 3			4. Draw 3 hexagons			6. Draw 5 squares
		1. 1 3/9			5. Draw strip of 5 spaces			
		2. 1 2/3			6. Draw 7 hexagons	97	7-9	1. Color 6 dots
		3. 2 1/4			7. Draw 8 triangles			2. Color 2 hexagons
		4. 1 2/6			8. Draw 6 squares			3. Color 4 spaces
		5. 1 2/8						4. Draw 7 dots
		6. 1 6/7	91	7-5	1. Color 4			5. 3/9
		7. 2 2/5			2. Color 3			6. Draw 5 rectangles
		8. 2 1/2			3. Color 2 dots			
					4. Color 6 triangles			
		Part 4			5. Color 4 spaces			
		1. 8/5			6. Color 2 hexagons			
		2. 8/6			7. Color 5 squares			
		3. 5/4			8. Color 6 dots			
		4. 8/3						
		5. 9/7						
		6. 13/8						
		7. 5/2						
		8. 7/4						

Page	Resource		Page	Resource		Page	Resource	
106	8-3	1. 1/5	121	9-2	1. 2/4	124	9-5	7. 4/8
		2. 1/3			2. 3/6			8. 6/15
		3. 1/4			3. 5/10			9. 4/16
		4. 5/6			4. 4/6			10. 15/20
		5. 7/8			5. 6/9			11. 2/5
		6. 1/3			6. 8/12			12. 1/2
		7. 4/5			7. 6/8			13. 4/7
		8. 1/2			8. 9/12	125	9-5	14. 2/3
		9. 2/3			9. 12/16			15. 3/4
		10. 1/3			10. 3/6			16. 2/3
		11. 2/3			11. 4/8			17. 5/7
		12. 5/6			12. 6/9			18. 2/3
		13. 2/8			13. 8/12			
		14. 1/3			14. 9/12	146	10-4	1. 3/4
		15. 4/7			15. 12/16			2. 2/3
		16. 3/4			16. 6/8			3. 7/8
								4. 3/5
107	8-4	1. 1/2, 1/3, 1/5, 1/7, 1/9, 1/10	122	9-3	1. 2/4 = 3/6			5. 5/6
		2. 1/10, 4/9, 2/3, 3/4, 7/8, 11/12			2. 2/6 = 3/9			6. 5/7
					3. 2/8 = 3/12			7. 4/8 or 1/2
					4. 4/6 = 6/9			8. 5/9
108	8-5	1. Close to 4			5. 4/10 = 6/15			9. 5/6
		2. Close to 4 1/2			6. 8/10 = 12/15			10. 4/4 or 1
		3. Close to 6			7. 14/16 = 21/24			11. 6/9 or 2/3
		4. Close to 4 1/2			8. 10/12 = 15/18			12. 3/3 or 1
		5. Close to 4 1/2			9. 6/8 = 9/12			13. 7/8
		6. Close to 5 1/2			10. 6/4 = 9/6			14. 6/7
		7. Close to 3 1/2			11. 8/6 = 12/9			15. 9/10
		8. Close to 5 1/2			12. 6/10 = 9/15			16. 4/5
					13. 6/12 = 9/18			
109	8-6	1. 2/4			14. 14/18 = 21/27	147	10-5	1 5/4, 1 1/4
		2. 2/3			15. 18/20 = 27/30			2. 4/3, 1 1/3
		3. 2/4			16. 4/8 = 6/12			3. 11/8, 1 3/8
		4. 2/3						4. 7/5, 1 2/5
		5. 2/8	123	9-4	1. 2/3			5. 7/6, 1 1/6
		6. 2/5			2. 3/4			6. 9/7, 1 2/7
		7. 4/7			3. 7/8			7. 10/8, 1 2/8, 1 1/4
		8. 3/4			4. 2/3			8. 12/9, 1 3/9, 1 1/3
		9. 0			5. 3/4			9. 5/3, 1 2/3
		10. 1			6. 1/2			10. 6/4, 1 2/4, 1 1/2
		11. 1			7. 7/9			11. 11/9, 1 2/9
		12. 0			8. 1/6			12. 3/2, 1 1/2
		13. 1/2						13. 10/8, 1 2/8, 1 1/4
		14. 1/2	124	9-5	1. 3/6			14. 12/10, 1 2/10, 1 1/5
		15. 1			2. 5/10			15. 6/5, 1 1/5
		16. 0			3. 10/15			16. 15/12, 1 3/12, 1 1/4
					4. 9/12			
					5. 12/20			
					6. 6/12			

223

Page	Resource	
170	11-4	1. 3 5/8
		2. 3 5/6
		3. 3 3/4
		4. 4 5/8
		5. 3 6/8 or 3 3/4
		6. 4 7/10
		7. 3 3/4
		8. 3 4/6 or 3 2/3
		9. 4 4/8 or 4 1/2
		10. 3 9/10
		11. 3 7/12
		12. 5
171	11-5	1. 3 5/6
		2. 3 7/12
		3. 3 9/10
		4. 2 7/12
		5. 3 11/15
		6. 4 9/20
		7. 3 10/12 or 35/6
		8. 4 1/10
		9. 3 11/14
		10. 3 13/15
		11. 4 1/6
		12. 4 7/10
172	11-6	1. 4 1/6
		2. 3 9/14
		3. 5 1/10
		4. 4 5/12
		5. 4 2/15
		6. 5 3/20
		7. 4 1/12
		8. 4 3/10
		9. 4 5/14
		10. 4 4/15
		11. 4 1/6
		12. 2 11/12
173	11-7	1. 6 5/12
		2. 5 4/6 or 5 2/3
		3. 5 4/5
		4. 5 3/12 or 5 1/4
		5. 6 11/20
		6. 5 1/4
		7. 8 1/12
		8. 4 2/10 or 4 1/5
		9. 4 11/21

Page	Resource	
173	11-7	10. 4 3/10
		11. 4 1/6
		12. 5 1/30
174	11-8	1. 4 3/4
		2. 3 5/6
		3. 4 2/3
		4. 3 5/8
		5. 3 6/8 or 3 3/4
		6. 4 7/10
		7. 3 10/12 or 3 5/6
		8. 4 1/10
		9. 3 11/14
		10. 4 4/15
		11. 4 1/6
		12. 5 4/9
		13. 6 1/8
		14. 7 5/14
		15. 4 2/6 or 4 1/3
183	12-1	1. 1 1/4
		2. 1 1/6
		3. 1 1/3
		4. 3 1/10
		5. 1 2/4 or 1 1/2
		6. 1 3/8
		7. 1 2/9
		8. 5/9
		9. 1 2/5
		10. 1 1/3
		11. 2 4/6 or 2 2/3
		12. 1 3/5
		13. 2 2/8 or 2 1/4
		14. 3 2/7
		15. 1 3/7
184	12-2	1. 2/3
		2. 5/6
		3. 3/4
		4. 4/5
		5. 2/4 or 1/2
		6. 7/8
		7. 8/9
		8. 2/6 or 1/3
		9. 3/5
		10. 2/3
		11. 1 2/4 or 1 1/2
		12. 3/5
		13. 2/8 or 1/4

Page	Resource	
184	12-2	14. 5/7
		15. 4/7
185	12-3	1. 1 1/4
		2. 1 1/6
		3. 1 3/6 or 1 1/2
		4. 2 5/10 or 2 1/2
		5. 1 2/6 or 1 1/3
		6. 1 5/8
		7. 1
		8. 1
		9. 1 6/10 or 1 3/5
		10. 1 3/6 or 1 1/2
		11. 2 3/6 or 2 1/2
		12. 1 2/10 or 1 /5
		13. 2 1/8
		14. 3 2/14 or 3 /7
		15. 1 5/14
186	12-4	1. 1 1/6
		2. 1 1/12
		3. 1 1/6
		4. 1 3/10
		5. 1 4/15
		6. 1 7/20
		7. 2 1/10
		8. 1 5/12
		9. 1 6/20 or 1/10
		10. 1 1/6
		11. 2 5/14
		12. 1 11/20
		13. 2 13/24
		14. 2 2/15
		15. 1 11/21
187	12-5	1. 1 5/6
		2. 11/12
		3. 19/20
		4. 9/14
		5. 1 2/15
		6. 9/10
		7. 13/15
		8. 1 1/6
		9. 5/6
		10. 7/12
		11. 7/8
		12. 1 3/10
		13. 1 4/15
		14. 1 5/18
		15. 7/10

CPSIA information can be obtained
at www.ICGtesting.com
Printed in the USA
BVOW07s2241010616

450364BV00011B/66/P